SCOTT FORESMAN

Reading Street
COMMON CORE

Reading Street
Common Core
Writing
to Sources

Glenview, Illinois

Boston, Massachusetts

Chandler, Arizona

Upper Saddle River, New Jersey

ISBN-13: 978-0-328-76855-4
ISBN-10:   0-328-76855-3
4 5 6 7 8 9 10 VON4 16 15 14 13

Reading Street Common Core
Writing to Sources

Reading Street Common Core Writing to Sources makes fact-finding fun! Students substantiate their claims and communicate in writing what they have learned from one text and then from other related texts.

Reading Street Common Core Writing to Sources encourages students to collaborate and share their growing knowledge with peers, adding quality experiences in the art of using text-based evidence.

Reading Street Common Core Writing to Sources provides more practice with all modes of writing—argument, informative/explanatory, and narrative—and connects to the Common Core State Standards.

Reading Street Common Core Writing to Sources gives students opportunities to complete Performance Tasks by writing in response to what they read and collaborating with others.

Reading Street Common Core Writing to Sources offers you an alternative approach to writing tasks on Reading Street!

1 Write Like a Reporter
Write to one source.
Students respond to the main selection by citing evidence from the text.

2 Connect the Texts
Write to two sources.
Students respond to the main and paired selections by citing evidence from the texts.

3 Prove It! Unit Writing Task
Write to multiple sources.
Students analyze multiple sources within a unit and cite evidence from the texts.

4 More Connect the Texts
Additional lessons specific to writing forms within all modes of writing—argument, informative/explanatory, and narrative—are included.

"Write Like a Reporter!"

Table of Contents

Get Ready for Performance Tasks

Unit R My World

Writing Focus: Narrative

Write Like a Reporter

Narrative

> **Student Prompt** Reread *Sam*. Then look at page 21. Where is Tam? Write about the things you see.

_____

- -

_____

- -

_____

- -

_____

- -

_____

- -

_____

- -

_____

- -

_____

- -

_____

- -

_____

Write Like a Reporter
Narrative

> **Student Prompt, p. 6** Reread *Sam.* Then look at page 21. Where is Tam? Write about the things you see.

Writing to Sources Have children reread the story. Then have them look at page 21. Using the image and the text, ask them to describe Tam and tell what he is doing. Provide a sentence frame: *I see ____. ____ is on the bed.* Have children use the sentence frames to write a short story or create their own sentences for the story to tell about Tam. Ask children to share their stories with the group.

Children's sentences should:

- provide a setting and character
- include a sequence of events that is true to those in the text
- use descriptive words that identify the events
- demonstrate strong command of the conventions of standard written English

---

© **Common Core State Standards**

Writing 3. Write narratives in which they recount two or more appropriately sequenced events, include some details regarding what happened, use temporal words to signal event order, and provide some sense of closure.

Connect the Texts

Narrative

Student Prompt Tell what Sam does in *Sam.* Tell what Rip does in "Rip Van Winkle." Which actions could really happen? Write about the event.

_____

- -

_____

_____

- -

_____

_____

- -

_____

_____

- -

_____

_____

- -

_____

_____

- -

_____

_____

- -

_____

Connect the Texts
Narrative

> **Student Prompt, p. 8** Tell what Sam does in *Sam*. Tell what Rip does in "Rip Van Winkle." Which actions could really happen? Write about the event.

Writing to Sources Review the selections *Sam* and "Rip Van Winkle." Have children tell about Sam and Rip to identify which person could be real and which is make-believe. Then write about the events that could really happen. Use the following sentence frames if needed to help beginning writers: _____ *has a pet.* _____ *can play.*

4-point Narrative Writing Rubric					
Score	**Narrative Focus**	**Organization**	**Development of Narrative**	**Language and Vocabulary**	**Conventions**
4	Narrative is clearly focused and developed throughout.	Narrative has a well-developed, logical, easy-to-follow plot.	Narrative includes thorough and effective use of details, dialogue, and description.	Narrative uses precise, concrete sensory language as well as figurative language and/or domain-specific vocabulary.	Narrative has correct grammar, usage, spelling, capitalization, and punctuation.
3	Narrative is mostly focused and developed throughout.	Narrative has a plot, but there may be some lack of clarity and/or unrelated events.	Narrative includes adequate use of details, dialogue and description.	Narrative uses adequate sensory and figurative language and/or domain-specific vocabulary.	Narrative has a few errors but is completely understandable.
2	Narrative is somewhat developed but may occasionally lose focus.	Narrative's plot is difficult to follow, and ideas are not connected well.	Narrative includes only a few details, dialogues, and descriptions.	Language in narrative is not precise or sensory; lacks domain-specific vocabulary.	Narrative has some errors in usage, grammar, spelling and/or punctuation.
1	Narrative may be confusing, unfocused, or too short.	Narrative has little or no apparent plot.	Narrative includes few or no details, dialogue or description.	Language in narrative is vague, unclear, or confusing.	Narrative is hard to follow because of frequent errors.
0	Narrative gets no credit if it does not demonstrate adequate command of narrative writing traits.				

Ⓒ **Common Core State Standards**

Writing 3. Write narratives in which they recount two or more appropriately sequenced events, include some details regarding what happened, use temporal words to signal event order, and provide some sense of closure.

Name_____

Write Like a Reporter
Narrative

> **Student Prompt** Look at pages 51 and 52 in *Snap!* Who comes to Sam's house? Write about what this person does.

_____
- -
_____
- -
_____
- -
_____
- -
_____
- -
_____
- -
_____
- -
_____
- -
_____
- -
_____

Write Like a Reporter
Narrative

> **Student Prompt, p. 10** Look at pages 51 and 52 in *Snap!* Who comes to Sam's house? Write about what this person does.

Writing to Sources Review *Snap!* with children. Using the images and the text, have them tell what Pam and Sam do (*tap, pat*). Then have them tell what Mac does. Have children write about what Mac does. If necessary provide a sentence frame: _____ *can* _____.

Children's sentences should:

- provide a setting and characters
- include events in sequence that reflect those in the text
- use words that express sensory detail when describing the events
- demonstrate strong command of the conventions of standard written English

ⓒ **Common Core State Standards**

Writing 3. Write narratives in which they recount two or more appropriately sequenced events, include some details regarding what happened, use temporal words to signal event order, and provide some sense of closure.

Name_____

Connect the Texts
Narrative

Student Prompt How are photographs important in both *Snap!* and "Families"? Draw pictures of a family from each selection doing something together. Write a sentence that tells about each picture.

_____

_____

_____

_____

_____

_____

_____

_____

_____

_____

_____

_____

_____

_____

Connect the Texts
Narrative

> **Student Prompt, p. 12** How are photographs important in both *Snap!* and "Families"? Draw pictures of a family from each selection doing something together. Write a sentence that tells about each picture.

Writing to Sources Review the selections *Snap!* and "Families." Have children find words and sentences to show how photographs are important. Ask them to describe the photographs. Then have children draw their pictures and write about the pictures.

			4-point Narrative Writing Rubric		
Score	**Narrative Focus**	**Organization**	**Development of Narrative**	**Language and Vocabulary**	**Conventions**
4	Narrative is clearly focused and developed throughout.	Narrative has a well-developed, logical, easy-to-follow plot.	Narrative includes thorough and effective use of details, dialogue, and description.	Narrative uses precise, concrete sensory language as well as figurative language and/or domain-specific vocabulary.	Narrative has correct grammar, usage, spelling, capitalization, and punctuation.
3	Narrative is mostly focused and developed throughout.	Narrative has a plot, but there may be some lack of clarity and/or unrelated events.	Narrative includes adequate use of details, dialogue and description.	Narrative uses adequate sensory and figurative language and/or domain-specific vocabulary.	Narrative has a few errors but is completely understandable.
2	Narrative is somewhat developed but may occasionally lose focus.	Narrative's plot is difficult to follow, and ideas are not connected well.	Narrative includes only a few details, dialogues, and descriptions.	Language in narrative is not precise or sensory; lacks domain-specific vocabulary.	Narrative has some errors in usage, grammar, spelling and/or punctuation.
1	Narrative may be confusing, unfocused, or too short.	Narrative has little or no apparent plot.	Narrative includes few or no details, dialogue or description.	Language in narrative is vague, unclear, or confusing.	Narrative is hard to follow because of frequent errors.
0	Narrative gets no credit if it does not demonstrate adequate command of narrative writing traits.				

© Common Core State Standards

Writing 3. Write narratives in which they recount two or more appropriately sequenced events, include some details regarding what happened, use temporal words to signal event order, and provide some sense of closure.

Name_____

Write Like a Reporter
Narrative

> **Student Prompt** Look at page 79 in *Tip and Tam.*
> Where are Tip and Tam? Write about how Tip and
> Tam get in the bag.

Write Like a Reporter
Narrative

> **Student Prompt, p. 14** Look at page 79 in *Tip and Tam*. Where are Tip and Tam? Write about how Tip and Tam get in the bag.

Writing to Sources Ask children to retell the story *Tip and Tam.* On chart paper, make a list of the events they tell about. Then have children write about Tip and Tam, using the book for details as well as the events on the list. Remind children to use details from the text as they write.

Children's paragraphs should:

- provide a setting, narrator, and/or characters
- include a chronology of events true to those in the text
- elaborate using details and descriptive words that identify the plot
- demonstrate strong command of the conventions of standard written English

© **Common Core State Standards**

Writing 3. Write narratives in which they recount two or more appropriately sequenced events, include some details regarding what happened, use temporal words to signal event order, and provide some sense of closure.

Name_____

Narrative

Tip and Tam

Connect the Texts
Narrative

Student Prompt Which yard shown in the photo essay "Yards" is most like the yard in the story *Tip and Tam?* How are the yards alike? Choose a yard and write about it to identify the selection setting. Use the selection to help you give details.

_____

_____

_____

_____

_____

_____

_____

_____

_____

_____

_____

_____

_____

_____

_____

_____

Copyright © Pearson Education, Inc., or its affiliates. All Rights Reserved.

16 Unit R • Week 3 • *Tip and Tam*

Connect the Texts
Narrative

Student Prompt, p. 16 Which yard shown in the photo essay "Yards" is most like the yard in the story *Tip and Tam?* How are the yards alike? Choose a yard and write about it to identify the selection setting. Use the selection to help you give details.

Writing to Sources Have children review the yards in *Tip and Tam* and "Yards." Ask them to find how the yard in the story is like and unlike the yards in "Yards." Make a list of details they name (tree, people, flowers, toys, leaves, pets). Then have them write about a yard to tell about the selection setting in the yard.

		4-point Narrative Writing Rubric			
Score	Narrative Focus	Organization	Development of Narrative	Language and Vocabulary	Conventions
4	Narrative is clearly focused and developed throughout.	Narrative has a well-developed, logical, easy-to-follow plot.	Narrative includes thorough and effective use of details, dialogue, and description.	Narrative uses precise, concrete sensory language as well as figurative language and/or domain-specific vocabulary.	Narrative has correct grammar, usage, spelling, capitalization, and punctuation.
3	Narrative is mostly focused and developed throughout.	Narrative has a plot, but there may be some lack of clarity and/or unrelated events.	Narrative includes adequate use of details, dialogue and description.	Narrative uses adequate sensory and figurative language and/or domain-specific vocabulary.	Narrative has a few errors but is completely understandable.
2	Narrative is somewhat developed but may occasionally lose focus.	Narrative's plot is difficult to follow, and ideas are not connected well.	Narrative includes only a few details, dialogue, and description.	Language in narrative is not precise or sensory; lacks domain-specific vocabulary.	Narrative has some errors in usage, grammar, spelling and/or punctuation.
1	Narrative may be confusing, unfocused, or too short.	Narrative has little or no apparent plot.	Narrative includes few or no details, dialogue or description.	Language in narrative is vague, unclear, or confusing.	Narrative is hard to follow because of frequent errors.
0	Narrative gets no credit if it does not demonstrate adequate command of narrative writing traits.				

© Common Core State Standards

Writing 3. Write narratives in which they recount two or more appropriately sequenced events, include some details regarding what happened, use temporal words to signal event order, and provide some sense of closure.

Name_____

Write Like a Reporter
Narrative

> **Student Prompt** Look at pages 98 and 99 in *The Big Top.* What do Pam and Dot like to do? Write about the story events to tell why the girls sit on the mat.

_____

- -

_____

- -

_____

- -

_____

- -

_____

- -

_____

- -

_____

- -

_____

- -

Write Like a Reporter
Narrative

> **Student Prompt, p. 18** Look at pages 98 and 99 in *The Big Top*. What do Pam and Dot like to do? Write about the story events to tell why the girls sit on the mat.

Writing to Sources Have children tell what Pam and Dot do on page 98 of *The Big Top.* Then ask them to tell what the girls do next. Have children write about the events. Suggest that they include why the girls need to sit on the mat.

Children's sentences should:

- provide a setting and characters
- include a logical sequence of events that reflects those in the text
- use words that signify chronology in the retelling of events
- demonstrate strong command of the conventions of standard written English

---

Ⓒ **Common Core State Standards**

Writing 3. Write narratives in which they recount two or more appropriately sequenced events, include some details regarding what happened, use temporal words to signal event order, and provide some sense of closure.

Connect the Texts

Narrative

Student Prompt Review the signs in "Around the Block." Then look at the pages in *The Big Top.* What kinds of street signs might Pam and Dot see in their neighborhood? Pick a sign and write where Pam and Dot would find the sign in their neighborhood.

_____

- -

_____

- -

_____

- -

_____

- -

_____

- -

_____

- -

_____

- -

_____

- -

Connect the Texts
Narrative

Student Prompt, p. 20 Review the signs in "Around the Block." Then look at the pages in *The Big Top*. What kinds of street signs might Pam and Dot see in their neighborhood? Pick a sign and write where Pam and Dot would find the sign in their neighborhood.

Writing to Sources Have children discuss the signs and symbols they learned about in "Around the Block." Have children think about Dot and Pam's neighborhood in *The Big Top*. What kinds of street signs might they see? Then have them choose a sign and write about the sign. Have them include details from the selection as they write about the location of the sign and what the sign means to the girls.

4-point Narrative Writing Rubric					
Score	**Narrative Focus**	**Organization**	**Development of Narrative**	**Language and Vocabulary**	**Conventions**
4	Narrative is clearly focused and developed throughout.	Narrative has a well-developed, logical, easy-to-follow plot.	Narrative includes thorough and effective use of details, dialogue, and description.	Narrative uses precise, concrete sensory language as well as figurative language and/or domain-specific vocabulary.	Narrative has correct grammar, usage, spelling, capitalization, and punctuation.
3	Narrative is mostly focused and developed throughout.	Narrative has a plot, but there may be some lack of clarity and/or unrelated events.	Narrative includes adequate use of details, dialogue and description.	Narrative uses adequate sensory and figurative language and/or domain-specific vocabulary.	Narrative has a few errors but is completely understandable.
2	Narrative is somewhat developed but may occasionally lose focus.	Narrative's plot is difficult to follow, and ideas are not connected well.	Narrative includes only a few details, dialogues, and descriptions.	Language in narrative is not precise or sensory; lacks domain-specific vocabulary.	Narrative has some errors in usage, grammar, spelling and/or punctuation.
1	Narrative may be confusing, unfocused, or too short.	Narrative has little or no apparent plot.	Narrative includes few or no details, dialogue or description.	Language in narrative is vague, unclear, or confusing.	Narrative is hard to follow because of frequent errors.
0	Narrative gets no credit if it does not demonstrate adequate command of narrative writing traits.				

© Common Core State Standards

Writing 3. Write narratives in which they recount two or more appropriately sequenced events, include some details regarding what happened, use temporal words to signal event order, and provide some sense of closure.

Name

Write Like a Reporter
Narrative

Student Prompt Look at page 130 in *School Day.*
How can the children fix the broken toy? Write a story
that tells what Kim, Pat, and Jill do.

Write Like a Reporter
Narrative

> **Student Prompt, p. 22** Look at page 130 in *School Day.* How can the children fix the broken toy? Write a story that tells what Kim, Pat, and Jill do.

Writing to Sources Have children review the selection *School Day.* Direct their attention to page 130 and ask them to tell how all of the children can work together to help get the toy fixed. Using the images and text on pages 130 and 131, have volunteers tell what they see happening. Have children write their stories. Remind them to keep the events in order to show how the toy gets fixed. Ask volunteers to share their stories.

Children's sentences should:

- provide a setting, narrator, and/or characters
- include transitional strategies to retell the plot
- use descriptive words that identify the events in chronological order
- demonstrate strong command of the conventions of standard written English

Ⓒ **Common Core State Standards**

Writing 3. Write narratives in which they recount two or more appropriately sequenced events, include some details regarding what happened, use temporal words to signal event order, and provide some sense of closure.

Connect the Texts
Narrative

> **Student Prompt** How does Sam in *School Day* get to school? What ways to get to school are shown in the photo essay "How Do You Get to School?" Write a story about going to school. Use the words and pictures to give details.

_____

- -

_____

- -

_____

- -

_____

- -

_____

- -

_____

- -

_____

- -

_____

- -

_____

Connect the Texts
Narrative

> **Student Prompt, p. 24** How does Sam in *School Day* get to school? What ways to get to school are shown in the photo essay "How Do You Get to School?" Write a story about going to school. Use the words and pictures to give details.

Writing to Sources Have children compare Sam in *School Day* to the people in the photographs and explain how they each get to school. Ask children to tell about ways to get to school—walking, a bike ride, a bus ride, a car ride, a ride in a cart. Then have them choose a way and write a story about going to school. Remind children to use the words and pictures in the book to add details to their story.

		4-point Narrative Writing Rubric			
Score	**Narrative Focus**	**Organization**	**Development of Narrative**	**Language and Vocabulary**	**Conventions**
4	Narrative is clearly focused and developed throughout.	Narrative has a well-developed, logical, easy-to-follow plot.	Narrative includes thorough and effective use of details, dialogue, and description.	Narrative uses precise, concrete sensory language as well as figurative language and/or domain-specific vocabulary.	Narrative has correct grammar, usage, spelling, capitalization, and punctuation.
3	Narrative is mostly focused and developed throughout.	Narrative has a plot, but there may be some lack of clarity and/or unrelated events.	Narrative includes adequate use of details, dialogue and description.	Narrative uses adequate sensory and figurative language and/or domain-specific vocabulary.	Narrative has a few errors but is completely understandable.
2	Narrative is somewhat developed but may occasionally lose focus.	Narrative's plot is difficult to follow, and ideas are not connected well.	Narrative includes only a few details, dialogues, and descriptions.	Language in narrative is not precise or sensory; lacks domain-specific vocabulary.	Narrative has some errors in usage, grammar, spelling and/or punctuation.
1	Narrative may be confusing, unfocused, or too short.	Narrative has little or no apparent plot.	Narrative includes few or no details, dialogue or description.	Language in narrative is vague, unclear, or confusing.	Narrative is hard to follow because of frequent errors.
0	Narrative gets no credit if it does not demonstrate adequate command of narrative writing traits.				

© Common Core State Standards

Writing 3. Write narratives in which they recount two or more appropriately sequenced events, include some details regarding what happened, use temporal words to signal event order, and provide some sense of closure.

Name_____

Write Like a Reporter

Narrative

> **Student Prompt** Look at page 155 in the selection
> *Farmers Market.* What can you buy at a farmers
> market? Reread the story and write what Pam and
> Dad did. Keep the events in the same order as they
> are in the story.

_____

_____

_____

_____

_____

_____

_____

_____

_____

Write Like a Reporter
Narrative

> **Student Prompt, p. 26** Look at page 155 in the selection *Farmers Market.* What can you buy at a farmers market? Reread the story and write what Pam and Dad did. Keep the events in the same order as they are in the story.

Writing to Sources Page through *Farmers Market* with children. Have children identify the people and foods Pam and Dad see at the market. Make a list of the food (watermelon, apples, bananas, tomatoes, grapes, potatoes). Have children write about what Pam and Dad do and see at the market. Remind them to keep the events in the same order as they happen in the story.

Children's sentences should:

- provide a setting, narrator, and/or characters
- include events in a sequence that is true to those in the text
- use descriptive words that identify the events in detail
- demonstrate strong command of the conventions of standard written English

Ⓒ **Common Core State Standards**

Writing 3. Write narratives in which they recount two or more appropriately sequenced events, include some details regarding what happened, use temporal words to signal event order, and provide some sense of closure.

Name_____

Connect the Texts

Narrative

> **Student Prompt** When do *Farmers Market* and "The Maid and the Milk Pail" take place? Where do they take place? How do you know? Write about the setting of one of the stories.

_____
- -
_____
_____
- -
_____
_____
- -
_____
_____
- -
_____
_____
- -
_____
_____
- -
_____
_____
- -
_____
_____
- -
_____

Connect the Texts
Narrative

> **Student Prompt, p. 28** When do *Farmers Market* and "The Maid and the Milk Pail" take place? Where do they take place? How do you know? Write about the setting of one of the stories.

Writing to Sources Review the selections to help children recognize that *Farmers Market* takes place at a farmers market in modern times and "The Maid and the Milk Pail" takes place in the country in the past. Point out that they can use the illustrations to help determine the setting. Then have them write about the setting for one of the stories. Have children review the writing for each setting together.

	4-point Narrative Writing Rubric				
Score	**Narrative Focus**	**Organization**	**Development of Narrative**	**Language and Vocabulary**	**Conventions**
4	Narrative is clearly focused and developed throughout.	Narrative has a well-developed, logical, easy-to-follow plot.	Narrative includes thorough and effective use of details, dialogue, and description.	Narrative uses precise, concrete sensory language as well as figurative language and/or domain-specific vocabulary.	Narrative has correct grammar, usage, spelling, capitalization, and punctuation.
3	Narrative is mostly focused and developed throughout.	Narrative has a plot, but there may be some lack of clarity and/or unrelated events.	Narrative includes adequate use of details, dialogue and description.	Narrative uses adequate sensory and figurative language and/or domain-specific vocabulary.	Narrative has a few errors but is completely understandable.
2	Narrative is somewhat developed but may occasionally lose focus.	Narrative's plot is difficult to follow, and ideas are not connected well.	Narrative includes only a few details, dialogues, and descriptions.	Language in narrative is not precise or sensory; lacks domain-specific vocabulary.	Narrative has some errors in usage, grammar, spelling and/or punctuation.
1	Narrative may be confusing, unfocused, or too short.	Narrative has little or no apparent plot.	Narrative includes few or no details, dialogue or description.	Language in narrative is vague, unclear, or confusing.	Narrative is hard to follow because of frequent errors.
0	Narrative gets no credit if it does not demonstrate adequate command of narrative writing traits.				

@ **Common Core State Standards**

Writing 3. Write narratives in which they recount two or more appropriately sequenced events, include some details regarding what happened, use temporal words to signal event order, and provide some sense of closure.

Prove It!
Personal Narrative

Academic Vocabulary

A personal narrative is a story that the writer tells about something that happened in his or her own life.

ELL

Introduce Genre Write *story* on the board. Ask children to tell what a story is and to give examples. Explain that a story tells about someone or something. Then write *personal narrative*. Point out to children that a personal narrative is a story about you. Explain that in a personal narrative, you tell a story about something that happened to you. Discuss with children the key features of a personal narrative that appear on this page.

What I Like

Personal Narrative

In this unit, children have read examples of narrative writing and have had the opportunity to write in this mode. Remind children of texts and writing tasks (such as Write Like a Reporter and Connect the Texts) in which they have encountered and practiced narrative writing.

Key Features of a Personal Narrative

- tells about an interesting event in your life
- gives details that help readers understand the event
- uses the words *I, me,* and *my*
- uses words to show the sequence
- has a beginning, middle, and end

Writing Task Overview

Each unit writing task provides children with an opportunity to write using information from a selection they are reading. To successfully complete the task, children must understand, interpret, and evaluate the selection and create their own response.

What I Like

Part 1: Children will reread the selection identified from this unit. They will then respond to a question about the selection and discuss their written responses with partners.

Part 2: Children will work individually to plan, write, and revise their own personal narrative.

Scorable Products: evidence-based short response, personal narrative

What I Like: Writing Task – Short Response

Teacher Directions:

1. Introduce the Source Reread the following text in the Student Edition:

Sam

pp. 18–27

Explain to children that they will use the words and illustrations in this text to answer a question. Tell children that they will also write their own personal narratives that use information from the text.

2. Have children draw a picture of something Sam does in the story *Sam*.

3. Using evidence from the text, have children write or dictate an event from the story involving the character Sam.

 Common Core State Standards

Writing 3. Write narratives in which they recount two or more appropriately sequenced events, include some details regarding what happened, use temporal words to signal event order, and provide some sense of closure.

Scoring Information

Use the following 2-point scoring rubric to evaluate children's answers to the evidence-based short response question.

	Analysis Rubric
2	The response: • demonstrates the ability to identify a character and recognize details about what the character does • includes specific details that make reference to the text
1	The response: • demonstrates a limited ability to identify a character and recognize details about what the character does • includes some details that make reference to the text
0	A response receives no credit if it demonstrates no ability to identify a character or recognize details about what the character does.

Ⓒ **Common Core State Standards**

Writing 3. Write narratives in which they recount two or more appropriately sequenced events, include some details regarding what happened, use temporal words to signal event order, and provide some sense of closure.

Name _____

What I Like

Writing Task – Short Response

Reread *Sam*.

Think about what Sam does.

Draw a picture to show what Sam does.

Name _____

Write a sentence about your picture.

_____

- -

_____

- -

_____

- -

_____

- -

_____

- -

_____

- -

_____

- -

_____

- -

_____

- -

_____

Let's Discuss

After you have written your sentence, talk about your story.
Your teacher will assign you a partner or a small group.

What I Like: Writing Task – Personal Narrative

Teacher Directions:

1. Have children draw a picture of the character Sam from the story *Sam*.

2. Have children write or dictate an event from the story involving the character.

3. Scoring Information Use the scoring rubric on the next page to evaluate children's personal narratives.

© Common Core State Standards

Writing 3. Write narratives in which they recount two or more appropriately sequenced events, include some details regarding what happened, use temporal words to signal event order, and provide some sense of closure.

		Narrative Writing Rubric			
Score	Narrative Focus	Organization	Development of Narrative	Language and Vocabulary	Conventions
4	Narrative clearly tells what the character does.	Narrative has an easy-to-follow event (plot).	Narrative includes effective use of details.	Narrative uses sensory language.	Narrative has correct use of conventions.
3	Narrative tells what the character does.	Narrative has an event (plot).	Narrative includes adequate use of details.	Narrative uses some sensory language.	Narrative has a few errors but is completely understandable.
2	Narrative may tell a little about what the character does.	Narrative's event is confusing.	Narrative includes only a few details.	Language in narrative is not sensory.	Narrative has some errors in standard conventions.
1	Narrative may be confusing.	Narrative has little or no apparent plot.	Narrative includes few or no details.	Language in narrative is confusing.	Narrative is hard to follow because of frequent errors.
0	Narrative gets no credit if it does not demonstrate adequate command of narrative writing traits.				

ⓒ Common Core State Standards

Writing 3. Write narratives in which they recount two or more appropriately sequenced events, include some details regarding what happened, use temporal words to signal event order, and provide some sense of closure.

Name _____

What I Like

Writing Task – Personal Narrative

Write a personal narrative that tells about something you do.
You can use examples from the selection to get ideas for things you like to do.

_____

- -

_____

_____

- -

_____

Name _____

What I Like: Writing Task – Personal Narrative

Teacher Directions:

1. Publish Explain to children that publishing their writing is the last step in the writing process. If time permits, have children review one another's narratives and incorporate any comments their classmates have. Discuss different ways technology can be used to publish writing.

2. Present Children will now have the option to present their personal narratives. Have children give speeches on their personal narratives in front of the class. Use the list below to offer children tips on listening and speaking.

While Listening to a Classmate...
- Face the speaker to listen attentively.
- Think about what the speaker says.

While Speaking to Classmates...
- Determine your purpose for speaking.
- Have good posture and eye contact.
- Speak at an appropriate pace.

Things to Do Together...
- Ask and answer questions with detail.
- Build on each other's ideas.

© Common Core State Standards

Writing 3. Write narratives in which they recount two or more appropriately sequenced events, include some details regarding what happened, use temporal words to signal event order, and provide some sense of closure.

Unit 1 Animals, Tame and Wild

Writing Focus: Narrative

Name_____

Write Like a Reporter
Narrative

Student Prompt Look at pages 25, 27, and 29 in *Sam, Come Back!* Where does Sam run first? Where does Sam run next? Where does Sam run last? Write a story that tells where Sam runs. Use details from the story.

_____

_____

_____

_____

_____

_____

_____

_____

_____

_____

_____

_____

_____

_____

_____

Write Like a Reporter
Narrative

> **Student Prompt, p. 42** Look at pages 25, 27, and 29 in *Sam, Come Back!*
> Where does Sam run first? Where does Sam run next? Where does Sam run
> last? Write a story that tells where Sam runs. Use details from the story.

Writing to Sources Have children retell the events of the story as you page through the book together. Have them answer the questions about the three places where Sam runs. Ask children to provide details about the places. Have children write about the events and use selection details to verify the accuracy of the events they write about. Ask children to share their sentences with the group.

Children's sentences should:

- provide a setting and character
- include a logical sequence of events that reflects those in the text
- use details and time-order words that signify chronology in the elaboration of events
- demonstrate strong command of the conventions of standard written English

Ⓒ **Common Core State Standards**

Writing 3. Write narratives in which they recount two or more appropriately sequenced events, include some details regarding what happened, use temporal words to signal event order, and provide some sense of closure.

Name

Connect the Texts
Narrative

Student Prompt Review the story *Sam, Come Back!* for details about Sam. Then review the sing-along "Puppy Games" for details about the puppy. Write about the animals, using details from the selections.

_____

Connect the Texts
Narrative

> **Student Prompt, p. 44** Review the story *Sam, Come Back!* for details about Sam. Then review the sing-along "Puppy Games" for details about the puppy. Write about the animals, using details from the selections.

Writing to Sources As children review *Sam, Come Back!* and "Puppy Games," have them identify details from the selections that tell about the animals. On the board, make a T-chart with *Sam* and *Puppy* as headings. Record the details children tell about each animal. Suggest they use the chart to help them write about the animals. Remind them that the pictures in the selections also contain details they can use.

		4-point Narrative Writing Rubric			
Score	**Narrative Focus**	**Organization**	**Development of Narrative**	**Language and Vocabulary**	**Conventions**
4	Narrative is clearly focused and developed throughout.	Narrative has a well-developed, logical, easy-to-follow plot.	Narrative includes thorough and effective use of details, dialogue, and description.	Narrative uses precise, concrete sensory language as well as figurative language and/or domain-specific vocabulary.	Narrative has correct grammar, usage, spelling, capitalization, and punctuation.
3	Narrative is mostly focused and developed throughout.	Narrative has a plot, but there may be some lack of clarity and/or unrelated events.	Narrative includes adequate use of details, dialogue and description.	Narrative uses adequate sensory and figurative language and/or domain-specific vocabulary.	Narrative has a few errors but is completely understandable.
2	Narrative is somewhat developed but may occasionally lose focus.	Narrative's plot is difficult to follow, and ideas are not connected well.	Narrative includes only a few details, dialogues, and descriptions.	Language in narrative is not precise or sensory; lacks domain-specific vocabulary.	Narrative has some errors in usage, grammar, spelling and/or punctuation.
1	Narrative may be confusing, unfocused, or too short.	Narrative has little or no apparent plot.	Narrative includes few or no details, dialogue or description.	Language in narrative is vague, unclear, or confusing.	Narrative is hard to follow because of frequent errors.
0	Narrative gets no credit if it does not demonstrate adequate command of narrative writing traits.				

© Common Core State Standards

Writing 3. Write narratives in which they recount two or more appropriately sequenced events, include some details regarding what happened, use temporal words to signal event order, and provide some sense of closure.

Name_____

Write Like a Reporter
Narrative

Student Prompt Reread page 57 of *Pig in a Wig.*
What did you find out about how Pig feels? Write
about how Pig feels. Use evidence from the story.

_____

- -

_____

- -

_____

- -

_____

- -

_____

- -

_____

- -

_____

- -

_____

- -

_____

- -

Write Like a Reporter
Narrative

Student Prompt, p. 46 Reread page 57 of *Pig in a Wig.* What did you find out about how Pig feels? Write about how Pig feels. Use evidence from the story.

Writing to Sources Review the selection by having children retell the story. Then ask them to reread page 57 and provide details about Pig and how he feels. Have children write a short summary that gives details about how Pig feels. Remind them to look at the picture to find details.

Children's sentences should:

- provide a setting, narrator, and character
- include a chronology of events that reflects those in the text
- use descriptive words and sensory details in the retelling of events
- demonstrate strong command of the conventions of standard written English

---

© **Common Core State Standards**

Writing 3. Write narratives in which they recount two or more appropriately sequenced events, include some details regarding what happened, use temporal words to signal event order, and provide some sense of closure.

Name_____

Connect the Texts
Narrative

Student Prompt The pig in *Pig in a Wig* and the dog in "We Are Vets" both feel sick. Who helps them get better? How? Write a story to tell what the two animals do after they get better.

_____

- -

_____

- -

_____

- -

_____

- -

_____

- -

_____

- -

_____

- -

_____

- -

_____

- -

Connect the Texts
Narrative

Student Prompt, p. 48 The pig in *Pig in a Wig* and the dog in "We Are Vets" both feel sick. Who helps them get better? How? Write a story to tell what the two animals do after they get better.

Writing to Sources Have children look through the selections *Pig in a Wig* and "We Are Vets" to find words and sentences in the texts to tell who helps the animals and what those people do to make the animals feel better. Have children write the items in a sequence to tell the events from feeling sick to feeling better.

			4-point Narrative Writing Rubric		
Score	**Narrative Focus**	**Organization**	**Development of Narrative**	**Language and Vocabulary**	**Conventions**
4	Narrative is clearly focused and developed throughout.	Narrative has a well-developed, logical, easy-to-follow plot.	Narrative includes thorough and effective use of details, dialogue, and description.	Narrative uses precise, concrete sensory language as well as figurative language and/or domain-specific vocabulary.	Narrative has correct grammar, usage, spelling, capitalization, and punctuation.
3	Narrative is mostly focused and developed throughout.	Narrative has a plot, but there may be some lack of clarity and/or unrelated events.	Narrative includes adequate use of details, dialogue and description.	Narrative uses adequate sensory and figurative language and/or domain-specific vocabulary.	Narrative has a few errors but is completely understandable.
2	Narrative is somewhat developed but may occasionally lose focus.	Narrative's plot is difficult to follow, and ideas are not connected well.	Narrative includes only a few details, dialogues, and descriptions.	Language in narrative is not precise or sensory; lacks domain-specific vocabulary.	Narrative has some errors in usage, grammar, spelling and/or punctuation.
1	Narrative may be confusing, unfocused, or too short.	Narrative has little or no apparent plot.	Narrative includes few or no details, dialogue or description.	Language in narrative is vague, unclear, or confusing.	Narrative is hard to follow because of frequent errors.
0	Narrative gets no credit if it does not demonstrate adequate command of narrative writing traits.				

© **Common Core State Standards**

Writing 3. Write narratives in which they recount two or more appropriately sequenced events, include some details regarding what happened, use temporal words to signal event order, and provide some sense of closure.

Name_____

Write Like a Reporter
Narrative

Student Prompt Reread pages 79–82 of *The Big Blue Ox.* What are some things Ox can do to help? Write a story of the things Ox does. Be sure to use evidence from the story.

_____

_____

_____

_____

_____

_____

_____

_____

_____

_____

_____

_____

_____

_____

Write Like a Reporter
Narrative

> **Student Prompt, p. 50** Reread pages 79–82 of *The Big Blue Ox*. What are some things Ox can do to help? Write a story of the things Ox does. Be sure to use evidence from the story.

Writing to Sources Ask children to retell *The Big Blue Ox*. Have them identify facts in the story that tell how Ox can help. Make a list on chart paper. Then have children write a story to tell the things Ox can do to help. Remind them to use the list as they write to include details from *The Big Blue Ox*.

Children's paragraphs should:

- provide a setting, narrator, and/or characters
- have focus and include events that are true to those in the text
- use details and descriptive words that identify the events
- demonstrate strong command of the conventions of standard written English

Ⓒ **Common Core State Standards**

Writing 3. Write narratives in which they recount two or more appropriately sequenced events, include some details regarding what happened, use temporal words to signal event order, and provide some sense of closure.

Connect the Texts

Narrative

Student Prompt Reread *The Big Blue Ox* and "They Can Help." Tell about the animals in each story. Are the animals real or make-believe? Write a story about the real and the make-believe animal characters in *The Big Blue Ox* and "They Can Help."

_____

- -

_____

- -

_____

- -

_____

- -

_____

- -

_____

- -

_____

- -

_____

Connect the Texts
Narrative

Student Prompt, p. 52 Reread *The Big Blue Ox* and "They Can Help." Tell about the animals in each story. Are the animals real or make-believe? Write a story about the real and the make-believe animal characters in *The Big Blue Ox* and "They Can Help."

Writing to Sources Make a chart with *The Big Blue Ox* and "They Can Help" as headings. Have children tell things about the animals and how the animals are different. Then have them write about the real and make-believe animals. Suggest that they tell what the animal characters did and how that helped them identify what is real and what is make-believe.

			4-point Narrative Writing Rubric		
Score	**Narrative Focus**	**Organization**	**Development of Narrative**	**Language and Vocabulary**	**Conventions**
4	Narrative is clearly focused and developed throughout.	Narrative has a well-developed, logical, easy-to-follow plot.	Narrative includes thorough and effective use of details, dialogue, and description.	Narrative uses precise, concrete sensory language as well as figurative language and/or domain-specific vocabulary.	Narrative has correct grammar, usage, spelling, capitalization, and punctuation.
3	Narrative is mostly focused and developed throughout.	Narrative has a plot, but there may be some lack of clarity and/or unrelated events.	Narrative includes adequate use of details, dialogue and description.	Narrative uses adequate sensory and figurative language and/or domain-specific vocabulary.	Narrative has a few errors but is completely understandable.
2	Narrative is somewhat developed but may occasionally lose focus.	Narrative's plot is difficult to follow, and ideas are not connected well.	Narrative includes only a few details, dialogues, and descriptions.	Language in narrative is not precise or sensory; lacks domain-specific vocabulary.	Narrative has some errors in usage, grammar, spelling and/or punctuation.
1	Narrative may be confusing, unfocused, or too short.	Narrative has little or no apparent plot.	Narrative includes few or no details, dialogue or description.	Language in narrative is vague, unclear, or confusing.	Narrative is hard to follow because of frequent errors.
0	Narrative gets no credit if it does not demonstrate adequate command of narrative writing traits.				

© Common Core State Standards

Writing 3. Write narratives in which they recount two or more appropriately sequenced events, include some details regarding what happened, use temporal words to signal event order, and provide some sense of closure.

Name_____

Write Like a Reporter
Narrative

Student Prompt Reread *A Fox and a Kit.* What do the fox and her kit do? Write about the things they do. Be sure to keep the events in the same order as the selection.

_____

_____

_____

_____

_____

_____

_____

_____

_____

_____

_____

_____

_____

_____

Write Like a Reporter
Narrative

> **Student Prompt, p. 54** Reread *A Fox and a Kit.* What do the fox and her kit do? Write about the things they do. Be sure to keep the events in the same order as the selection.

Writing to Sources Ask children to reread *A Fox and a Kit,* stopping after each page for children to tell what the fox and kit do. Then have them use the events to write a story. Remind them to keep the events in the same order as the selection. Have children share their stories with the group.

Children's sentences should:

- provide a setting and character
- include events in a sequence that reflects those in the text
- use descriptive words that identify the events
- demonstrate strong command of the conventions of standard written English

---

© Common Core State Standards

Writing 3. Write narratives in which they recount two or more appropriately sequenced events, include some details regarding what happened, use temporal words to signal event order, and provide some sense of closure.

Name_____

Connect the Texts
Narrative

> **Student Prompt** Review the selections "The Fox and the Grapes" and *A Fox and a Kit.* Tell about each fox. Then write sentences to tell what the foxes do. Use evidence from each selection in your writing.

_____
- -
_____
_____
- -
_____
_____
- -
_____
_____
- -
_____
_____
- -
_____
_____
- -
_____
_____
- -
_____

Connect the Texts
Narrative

Student Prompt, p. 56 Review the selections "The Fox and the Grapes" and *A Fox and a Kit.* Tell about each fox. Then write sentences to tell what the foxes do. Use evidence from each selection in your writing.

Writing to Sources Have children find words and sentences in the texts of *A Fox and a Kit* and "The Fox and the Grapes" to tell what the foxes do. Ask children to tell the differences between real and make-believe foxes. Then have them write what the foxes do. Remind them to use story details in their writing.

	4-point Narrative Writing Rubric				
Score	**Narrative Focus**	**Organization**	**Development of Narrative**	**Language and Vocabulary**	**Conventions**
4	Narrative is clearly focused and developed throughout.	Narrative has a well-developed, logical, easy-to-follow plot.	Narrative includes thorough and effective use of details, dialogue, and description.	Narrative uses precise, concrete sensory language as well as figurative language and/or domain-specific vocabulary.	Narrative has correct grammar, usage, spelling, capitalization, and punctuation.
3	Narrative is mostly focused and developed throughout.	Narrative has a plot, but there may be some lack of clarity and/or unrelated events.	Narrative includes adequate use of details, dialogue and description.	Narrative uses adequate sensory and figurative language and/or domain-specific vocabulary.	Narrative has a few errors but is completely understandable.
2	Narrative is somewhat developed but may occasionally lose focus.	Narrative's plot is difficult to follow, and ideas are not connected well.	Narrative includes only a few details, dialogues, and descriptions.	Language in narrative is not precise or sensory; lacks domain-specific vocabulary.	Narrative has some errors in usage, grammar, spelling and/or punctuation.
1	Narrative may be confusing, unfocused, or too short.	Narrative has little or no apparent plot.	Narrative includes few or no details, dialogue or description.	Language in narrative is vague, unclear, or confusing.	Narrative is hard to follow because of frequent errors.
0	Narrative gets no credit if it does not demonstrate adequate command of narrative writing traits.				

Ⓒ Common Core State Standards

Writing 3. Write narratives in which they recount two or more appropriately sequenced events, include some details regarding what happened, use temporal words to signal event order, and provide some sense of closure.

Write Like a Reporter

Narrative

Student Prompt Look at pages 134 and 135. Retell
this part of the story by writing about how Brad and
Kim save the red bird's egg. Use details from *Get the
Egg!* in your story.

_____

_____

_____

_____

_____

_____

_____

_____

_____

_____

Write Like a Reporter
Narrative

> **Student Prompt, p. 58** Look at pages 134 and 135. Retell this part of the story by writing about how Brad and Kim save the red bird's egg. Use details from *Get the Egg!* in your story.

Writing to Sources Review pages 134–135 with children. Using the images and the text, ask volunteers to tell what happened on the pages. Ask children to use their own words and details about Brad and Kim to rewrite this event of the story. Have volunteers share their stories.

Children's sentences should:

- provide a setting, narrator, and/or characters
- include a chronological order of events that reflects those in the text
- paraphrase the story events, using descriptive words and details
- demonstrate strong command of the conventions of standard written English

---

ⓒ Common Core State Standards

Writing 3. Write narratives in which they recount two or more appropriately sequenced events, include some details regarding what happened, use temporal words to signal event order, and provide some sense of closure.

Name_____

Connect the Texts

Narrative

Student Prompt How are Brad and Kim in *Get the Egg!* like the girl in "Help the Birds"? Write a story about the people in the selections to tell how they help animals. Use details from the selections.

_____

_____

_____

_____

_____

_____

_____

_____

_____

_____

_____

_____

_____

_____

_____

_____

_____

_____

_____

_____

_____

_____

Connect the Texts
Narrative

> **Student Prompt, p. 60** How are Brad and Kim in *Get the Egg!* like the girl in "Help the Birds"? Write a story about the people in the selections to tell how they help animals. Use details from the selections.

Writing to Sources After children review the events in *Get the Egg!* and "Help the Birds," ask them to tell what the people in the stories do to help animals. Have them write about it using information from the selections and the pictures. Ask volunteers to share their stories.

			4-point Narrative Writing Rubric		
Score	Narrative Focus	Organization	Development of Narrative	Language and Vocabulary	Conventions
4	Narrative is clearly focused and developed throughout.	Narrative has a well-developed, logical, easy-to-follow plot.	Narrative includes thorough and effective use of details, dialogue, and description.	Narrative uses precise, concrete sensory language as well as figurative language and/or domain-specific vocabulary.	Narrative has correct grammar, usage, spelling, capitalization, and punctuation.
3	Narrative is mostly focused and developed throughout.	Narrative has a plot, but there may be some lack of clarity and/or unrelated events.	Narrative includes adequate use of details, dialogue and description.	Narrative uses adequate sensory and figurative language and/or domain-specific vocabulary.	Narrative has a few errors but is completely understandable.
2	Narrative is somewhat developed but may occasionally lose focus.	Narrative's plot is difficult to follow, and ideas are not connected well.	Narrative includes only a few details, dialogue, and description.	Language in narrative is not precise or sensory; lacks domain-specific vocabulary.	Narrative has some errors in usage, grammar, spelling and/or punctuation.
1	Narrative may be confusing, unfocused, or too short.	Narrative has little or no apparent plot.	Narrative includes few or no details, dialogue or description.	Language in narrative is vague, unclear, or confusing.	Narrative is hard to follow because of frequent errors.
0	Narrative gets no credit if it does not demonstrate adequate command of narrative writing traits.				

© Common Core State Standards

Writing 3. Write narratives in which they recount two or more appropriately sequenced events, include some details regarding what happened, use temporal words to signal event order, and provide some sense of closure.

Write Like a Reporter
Narrative

Student Prompt Look at the photographs in *Animal Park.* Write about the animals in the park. Write a sentence for each animal. Keep the animals in the same order as they are in the selection.

Write Like a Reporter
Narrative

> **Student Prompt, p. 62** Look at the photographs in *Animal Park*. Write about the animals in the park. Write a sentence for each animal. Keep the animals in the same order as they are in the selection.

Writing to Sources Page through the selection with children. Write the following sentence frame on the board: *The _____ can _____.* Ask children to complete the sentence for several pictures. Then let them continue independently. Have children work together to review the sentences about each animal.

Children's sentences should:

- provide a setting and characters
- include events that are true to those in the text
- use descriptive words and details that identify the events
- demonstrate strong command of the conventions of standard written English

Ⓒ **Common Core State Standards**

Writing 3. Write narratives in which they recount two or more appropriately sequenced events, include some details regarding what happened, use temporal words to signal event order, and provide some sense of closure.

Name

Connect the Texts
Narrative

Student Prompt How are the animals in *Animal Park* and the animals in the poems alike? How are they different? Choose an animal and tell what it does.

Connect the Texts
Narrative

> **Student Prompt, p. 64** How are the animals in *Animal Park* and the animals in the poems alike? How are they different? Choose an animal and tell what it does.

Writing to Sources Review *Animal Park* and the poems. Have children give details from the text about each animal. Then have them choose an animal and use pictures, words, and sentences to tell about that animal. Children may elect to write a poem, such as *Big birds run in the hot sun!*

			4-point Narrative Writing Rubric		
Score	**Narrative Focus**	**Organization**	**Development of Narrative**	**Language and Vocabulary**	**Conventions**
4	Narrative is clearly focused and developed throughout.	Narrative has a well-developed, logical, easy-to-follow plot.	Narrative includes thorough and effective use of details, dialogue, and description.	Narrative uses precise, concrete sensory language as well as figurative language and/or domain-specific vocabulary.	Narrative has correct grammar, usage, spelling, capitalization, and punctuation.
3	Narrative is mostly focused and developed throughout.	Narrative has a plot, but there may be some lack of clarity and/or unrelated events.	Narrative includes adequate use of details, dialogue and description.	Narrative uses adequate sensory and figurative language and/or domain-specific vocabulary.	Narrative has a few errors but is completely understandable.
2	Narrative is somewhat developed but may occasionally lose focus.	Narrative's plot is difficult to follow, and ideas are not connected well.	Narrative includes only a few details, dialogues, and descriptions.	Language in narrative is not precise or sensory; lacks domain-specific vocabulary.	Narrative has some errors in usage, grammar, spelling and/or punctuation.
1	Narrative may be confusing, unfocused, or too short.	Narrative has little or no apparent plot.	Narrative includes few or no details, dialogue or description.	Language in narrative is vague, unclear, or confusing.	Narrative is hard to follow because of frequent errors.
0	Narrative gets no credit if it does not demonstrate adequate command of narrative writing traits.				

Ⓒ Common Core State Standards

Writing 3. Write narratives in which they recount two or more appropriately sequenced events, include some details regarding what happened, use temporal words to signal event order, and provide some sense of closure.

Prove It!
Story

Academic Vocabulary

A story tells about characters, and it tells what the characters do.

ELL

Introduce Genre Write *story* on the board. Explain that this word is used to identify writing about someone or something. Remind children that a story tells about the people in the story and it tells what they do. The people or animals are called characters. Discuss with children the key features of a story that appear on this page.

About Animals

Story

In this unit, children have read examples of narrative writing, including many stories, and have had the opportunity to write in this mode. Remind children of texts and writing tasks (such as Write Like a Reporter and Connect the Texts) in which they have encountered and practiced narrative writing.

Key Features of a Story
- uses characters to tell the story
- tells about an interesting event
- includes detail words to describe characters and events
- has a beginning, middle, and end

Writing Task Overview

Each unit writing task provides children with an opportunity to write using information from a selection they are reading. To successfully complete the task, children must understand, interpret, and evaluate the selection and create their own response.

About Animals

Part 1: Children will read the selection identified from this unit. They will then respond to several questions about the selection and discuss their written responses with partners or in small groups.

Part 2: Children will work individually to plan, write, and revise their own story.

Scorable Products: evidence-based short response, story

About Animals: Writing Task – Short Response

Teacher Directions:

1. Introduce the Source Reread the following selection in the Student Edition:

The Big Blue Ox

pp. 74–83

Explain to children that they will use the words and illustrations in the book to answer a question. Tell children that they will also write their own stories that use the characters from the text.

2. Have children draw a picture of the main character in *The Big Blue Ox.*

3. Using evidence from the text, have children write or dictate an event from the story involving the main character.

Scoring Information

Use the following 2-point scoring rubric to evaluate children's answers to the evidence-based short response question.

Tell about the main character in the selection *The Big Blue Ox.*

	Analysis Rubric
2	The response: • demonstrates the ability to identify and analyze the main character and tell about what the animal character does • includes specific details that make reference to the text
1	The response: • demonstrates a limited ability to identify and analyze the main character and tell about what the animal character does • includes some details that make reference to the text
0	A response receives no credit if it demonstrates no ability to identify and analyze the main character and tell about what the animal character does.

Ⓒ **Common Core State Standards**

Writing 3. Write narratives in which they recount two or more appropriately sequenced events, include some details regarding what happened, use temporal words to signal event order, and provide some sense of closure.

About Animals

Writing Task – Short Response

Draw a picture of the main character in
The Big Blue Ox.

Name _____

Write a sentence to tell about the animal character.

_____
- -
_____

_____
- -
_____

_____
- -
_____

_____
- -
_____

_____
- -
_____

_____
- -
_____

_____
- -
_____

Let's Discuss

After you have drawn your picture and written your sentence, discuss your ideas.
Your teacher will assign you a partner or a small group.

About Animals: Writing Task – Story

Teacher Directions:

1. Have children draw a picture of the animal characters in *The Big Blue Ox.*

2. Have children write or dictate sentences using information from the selection to tell about the animal characters.

3. Scoring Information Use the scoring rubric on the next page to evaluate children's stories.

© Common Core State Standards

Writing 3. Write narratives in which they recount two or more appropriately sequenced events, include some details regarding what happened, use temporal words to signal event order, and provide some sense of closure.

	Narrative Writing Rubric				
Score	Narrative Focus	Organization	Development of Narrative	Language and Vocabulary	Conventions
4	Narrative is correctly focused on a character.	Narrative has an easy-to-follow event (plot).	Narrative includes effective use of details.	Narrative uses sensory language.	Narrative has correct use of conventions.
3	Narrative is mostly focused on a character.	Narrative has an event (plot).	Narrative includes adequate use of details.	Narrative uses some sensory language.	Narrative has a few errors but is completely understandable.
2	Narrative is somewhat focused on a character.	Narrative's event is confusing.	Narrative includes only a few details.	Language in narrative is not sensory.	Narrative has some errors in basic conventions.
1	Narrative may be confusing or unfocused.	Narrative has little or no apparent plot.	Narrative includes few or no details.	Language in narrative is vague or confusing.	Narrative is hard to follow because of frequent errors.
0	Narrative gets no credit if it does not demonstrate adequate command of narrative writing traits.				

Ⓒ **Common Core State Standards**

Writing 3. Write narratives in which they recount two or more appropriately sequenced events, include some details regarding what happened, use temporal words to signal event order, and provide some sense of closure.

Name _____

About Animals

Writing Task – Story

Draw a picture of the animal characters in *The Big Blue Ox.* Write a story about animals and what they do. Use examples from the selection to highlight what they can do.

About Animals: Writing Task – Story

Teacher Directions:

1. Publish Explain to children that publishing their writing is the last step in the writing process. If time permits, have children review one another's compositions and incorporate any comments their classmates have. Discuss different ways technology can be used to publish writing.

2. Present Children will now have the option to present their stories. Have children give speeches on their stories in front of the class. Use the list below to offer children some tips on listening and speaking.

While Listening to a Classmate...
- Face the speaker to listen attentively.
- Take notes on what the speaker says.

While Speaking to Classmates...
- Determine your purpose for speaking.
- Have good posture and eye contact.
- Speak at an appropriate pace.

Things to Do Together...
- Ask and answer questions with detail.
- Build on each other's ideas.

© Common Core State Standards

Writing 3. Write narratives in which they recount two or more appropriately sequenced events, include some details regarding what happened, use temporal words to signal event order, and provide some sense of closure.

Unit 2 Communities

Writing Focus: Informative/Explanatory

Name_____

Write Like a Reporter

Informative/Explanatory

Student Prompt How do Max and Grandma get a big fish? Look back at pages 30 and 31 in *A Big Fish for Max*. Write about the steps in order. Use details from the story to write the steps.

_____

_____

_____

_____

_____

_____

_____

_____

_____

_____

_____

_____

Write Like a Reporter

Informative/Explanatory

> **Student Prompt, p. 78** How do Max and Grandma get a big fish? Look back at pages 30 and 31 in *A Big Fish for Max*. Write about the steps in order. Use details from the story to write the steps.

Writing to Sources Have children turn to page 22 and reread the page. Ask them what Max wants and what Grandma suggests they do. Have children retell the events of the story as you page through pages 23–29. Review pages 30–31 and have children retell the events. Ask them to write about how Max and Grandma get the fish. Remind children to use selection details. Ask them to share their writing with the group.

Children's sentences should:

- identify and focus on a topic
- use an effective text structure to describe a chronology of events
- support key ideas with details and evidence from the text
- demonstrate strong command of the conventions of standard written English

Ⓒ **Common Core State Standards**

Writing 2. Write informative/explanatory texts in which they name a topic, supply some facts about the topic, and provide some sense of closure.

A Big Fish for Max • Unit 2 • Week 1   **79**

Connect the Texts

Explanatory Comparison

> **Student Prompt** What does the family in *A Big Fish for Max* like to do? What does the family in "At Home" like to do? Write a comparison of the two families. Use details from the selections to support your ideas.

_____

_____

_____

_____

_____

_____

_____

_____

_____

_____

_____

_____

_____

_____

_____

_____

_____

_____

Connect the Texts
Informative/Explanatory Comparison

Student Prompt, p. 80 What does the family in *A Big Fish for Max* like to do? What does the family in "At Home" like to do? Write a comparison of the two families. Use details from the selections to support your ideas.

Writing to Sources Have children look at what the families in *A Big Fish for Max* and "At Home" do and then compare the activities. How are the families' activities alike? How are they different? Children may note that both families like to spend time together, while the family in *A Big Fish for Max* likes to eat fish and the family in "At Home" likes to work outside. Have children share their comparisons with the group.

Score	Focus	Organization	Development of Evidence	Language and Vocabulary	Conventions
	Informative/Explanatory Writing Rubric				
4	Main idea is clearly conveyed and well supported; response is focused.	Organization is clear and effective, creating a sense of cohesion.	Evidence is relevant and thorough; includes facts and details.	Ideas are clearly and effectively conveyed, using precise language and/or domain-specific vocabulary.	Command of conventions is strongly demonstrated.
3	Main idea is clear, adequately supported; response is generally focused.	Organization is clear, though minor flaws may be present and some ideas may be disconnected.	Evidence is adequate and includes facts and details.	Ideas are adequately conveyed, using both precise and more general language; may include domain-specific vocabulary.	Command of conventions is sufficiently demonstrated.
2	Main idea is somewhat supported; lacks focus or includes unnecessary material.	Organization is inconsistent, and flaws are apparent.	Evidence is uneven or incomplete; insufficient use of facts and details.	Ideas are unevenly conveyed, using overly-simplistic language; lacks domain-specific vocabulary.	Command of conventions is uneven.
1	Response may be confusing, unfocused; main idea insufficiently supported.	Organization is poor or nonexistent.	Evidence is poor or nonexistent.	Ideas are conveyed in a vague, unclear, or confusing manner.	There is very little command of conventions.
0	The response shows no evidence of the ability to construct a coherent explanatory essay using information from sources.				

© Common Core State Standards

Writing 2. Write informative/explanatory texts in which they name a topic, supply some facts about the topic, and provide some sense of closure.

Name_____

Write Like a Reporter

Informative/Explanatory

Student Prompt Review *The Farmer in the Hat* and tell what the children are doing. Write an explanation of the things the class did to get ready for the play. End your explanation with a closing statement of what may have happened had they not prepared for the play.

_____

_____

_____

_____

_____

_____

_____

_____

_____

_____

_____

_____

_____

_____

_____

Write Like a Reporter
Informative/Explanatory

Student Prompt, p. 82 Review *The Farmer in the Hat* and tell what the children are doing. Write an explanation of the things the class did to get ready for the play. End your explanation with a closing statement of what may have happened had they not prepared for the play.

Writing to Sources Have children tell what each character in *The Farmer in the Hat* did to get ready for the play. Turn to page 54 and review the page. Have children tell what Beth did and record that item in a list. Continue through the story, having children retell the events. Then have them write what the class did to get ready for the play. Remind children to include a closing statement. Ask them to share their writing with the group.

Children's sentences should:

- identify and focus on a topic
- provide a logical sequence using descriptive details about the topic
- provide a sense of closure by drawing conclusions based on evidence from the text
- demonstrate strong command of the conventions of standard written English

© Common Core State Standards

Writing 2. Write informative/explanatory texts in which they name a topic, supply some facts about the topic, and provide some sense of closure.

Connect the Texts

Informative/Explanatory

Student Prompt In *The Farmer in the Hat* and "Helping Hands at 4-H," groups of children work together. What is each group trying to do? Why? The children in both groups work well together. Why is that important? Write your ideas. Use information from the text.

_____

_____

_____

_____

_____

_____

_____

_____

_____

Connect the Texts
Informative/Explanatory

Student Prompt, p. 84 In *The Farmer in the Hat* and "Helping Hands at 4-H," groups of children work together. What is each group trying to do? Why? The children in both groups work well together. Why is that important? Write your ideas. Use information from the text.

Writing to Sources Have children find words and sentences in the texts of *The Farmer in the Hat* and "Helping Hands at 4-H" to tell how each group is working together. What are the groups trying to do, and why? Children might note that it is important for the children in *The Farmer in the Hat* to work well together because they want their play to be good, and their teacher might be grading them. It is important for the children in "Helping Hands at 4-H" to work well together because the farm animals depend on them.

	Informative/Explanatory Writing Rubric				
Score	Focus	Organization	Development of Evidence	Language and Vocabulary	Conventions
4	Main idea is clearly conveyed and well supported; response is focused.	Organization is clear and effective, creating a sense of cohesion.	Evidence is relevant and thorough; includes facts and details.	Ideas are clearly and effectively conveyed, using precise language and/or domain-specific vocabulary.	Command of conventions is strongly demonstrated.
3	Main idea is clear, adequately supported; response is generally focused.	Organization is clear, though minor flaws may be present and some ideas may be disconnected.	Evidence is adequate and includes facts and details.	Ideas are adequately conveyed, using both precise and more general language; may include domain-specific vocabulary.	Command of conventions is sufficiently demonstrated.
2	Main idea is somewhat supported; lacks focus or includes unnecessary material.	Organization is inconsistent, and flaws are apparent.	Evidence is uneven or incomplete; insufficient use of facts and details.	Ideas are unevenly conveyed, using overly-simplistic language; lacks domain-specific vocabulary.	Command of conventions is uneven.
1	Response may be confusing, unfocused; main idea insufficiently supported.	Organization is poor or nonexistent.	Evidence is poor or nonexistent.	Ideas are conveyed in a vague, unclear, or confusing manner.	There is very little command of conventions.
0	The response shows no evidence of the ability to construct a coherent explanatory essay using information from sources.				

© Common Core State Standards

Writing 2. Write informative/explanatory texts in which they name a topic, supply some facts about the topic, and provide some sense of closure.

Write Like a Reporter

Explanatory Report

Student Prompt Turn to pages 86 and 87 of *Who Works Here?* and tell what each community worker does. Write about the job of one of the people you see.

_____

- -

_____

- -

_____

- -

_____

- -

_____

- -

_____

- -

_____

- -

_____

- -

_____

- -

_____

- -

_____

Write Like a Reporter

Informative/Explanatory Report

> **Student Prompt, p. 86** Turn to pages 86 and 87 of *Who Works Here?* and tell what each community worker does. Write about the job of one of the people you see.

Writing to Sources Have children tell what each community worker shown on pages 86 and 87 does in *Who Works Here?* Remind them to look at the selection page about the worker if needed for more information. Suggest they reread the words and also study the pictures to gain information. Then have them write about one of the workers and what that worker does in the community. Arrange a display with the articles for each community worker. Have children read their reports to the class.

Children's sentences should:

- identify and focus on a topic
- supply supporting facts and clear details about the topic
- use an effective text structure and precise words to support purpose
- demonstrate strong command of the conventions of standard written English

---

Ⓒ **Common Core State Standards**

Writing 2. Write informative/explanatory texts in which they name a topic, supply some facts about the topic, and provide some sense of closure.

Connect the Texts

Explanatory Directions

> **Student Prompt** Using the community workers from *Who Works Here?* and "Neighborhood Map," find the location on the map where you would find each of the community workers. Then write directions to follow to locate several of the workers. Write your directions in a numbered list.

_____

_____

_____

_____

_____

_____

_____

_____

_____

_____

_____

_____

_____

_____

Connect the Texts
Informative/Explanatory Directions

Student Prompt, p. 88 Using the community workers from *Who Works Here?* and "Neighborhood Map," find the location on the map where you would find each of the community workers. Then write directions to follow to locate several of the workers. Write your directions in a numbered list.

Writing to Sources Have children look through *Who Works Here?* to find workers and then look at the map to see where some workers could be located. Suggest that they start at the police station and give directions to travel to other locations to see other workers. Have children take turns reading their directions as children follow the route on the "Neighborhood Map" on page 101.

	Informative/Explanatory Writing Rubric				
Score	**Focus**	**Organization**	**Development of Evidence**	**Language and Vocabulary**	**Conventions**
4	Main idea is clearly conveyed and well supported; response is focused.	Organization is clear and effective, creating a sense of cohesion.	Evidence is relevant and thorough; includes facts and details.	Ideas are clearly and effectively conveyed, using precise language and/or domain-specific vocabulary.	Command of conventions is strongly demonstrated.
3	Main idea is clear, adequately supported; response is generally focused.	Organization is clear, though minor flaws may be present and some ideas may be disconnected.	Evidence is adequate and includes facts and details.	Ideas are adequately conveyed, using both precise and more general language; may include domain-specific vocabulary.	Command of conventions is sufficiently demonstrated.
2	Main idea is somewhat supported; lacks focus or includes unnecessary material.	Organization is inconsistent, and flaws are apparent.	Evidence is uneven or incomplete; insufficient use of facts and details.	Ideas are unevenly conveyed, using overly-simplistic language; lacks domain-specific vocabulary.	Command of conventions is uneven.
1	Response may be confusing, unfocused; main idea insufficiently supported.	Organization is poor or nonexistent.	Evidence is poor or nonexistent.	Ideas are conveyed in a vague, unclear, or confusing manner.	There is very little command of conventions.
0	The response shows no evidence of the ability to construct a coherent explanatory essay using information from sources.				

© Common Core State Standards

Writing 2. Write informative/explanatory texts in which they name a topic, supply some facts about the topic, and provide some sense of closure.

Write Like a Reporter
Explanatory Paragraph

Student Prompt Review pages 124 and 125 of *The Big Circle* to see how the herd of triceratops works together to help each other. Write a short paragraph about what the animals did to be safe from T. Rex. Give evidence from the story to support your answer.

_____

_____

_____

_____

_____

_____

_____

_____

_____

_____

_____

_____

_____

_____

Write Like a Reporter
Informative/Explanatory Paragraph

Student Prompt, p. 90 Review pages 124 and 125 of *The Big Circle* to see how the herd of triceratops works together to help each other. Write a short paragraph about what the animals did to be safe from T. Rex. Give evidence from the story to support your answer.

Writing to Sources Have children retell *The Big Circle*, pointing out what T. Rex wanted. Then review the events on pages 124 and 125 and how the herd of triceratops works together to keep safe. Remind them to look at the words on the selection page and the pictures for more information to write what the animals did. Have children read their reports to the class.

Children's paragraphs should:
- introduce and focus on a topic
- supply some facts and details about the topic
- support key ideas with evidence from the text
- demonstrate strong command of the conventions of standard written English

Ⓒ Common Core State Standards

Writing 2. Write informative/explanatory texts in which they name a topic, supply some facts about the topic, and provide some sense of closure.

Connect the Texts

Explanatory Text

> **Student Prompt** How is what happens in *The Big Circle* similar to what happens in "We Are Safe Together"? Write the facts you learned in *The Big Circle* and "We Are Safe Together" about how animals stay safe.

_____

_____

_____

_____

_____

_____

_____

_____

_____

_____

_____

_____

_____

_____

_____

_____

_____

_____

_____

_____

Connect the Texts
Informative/Explanatory Text

> **Student Prompt, p. 92** How is what happens in *The Big Circle* similar to what happens in "We Are Safe Together"? Write the facts you learned in *The Big Circle* and "We Are Safe Together" about how animals stay safe.

Writing to Sources Have children find similarities between "We Are Safe Together" and *The Big Circle*. Ask them to tell how the animals stayed safe. Make a list of the animals in the stories and have children tell what they did to be safe. Record the information by each animal group. Then have children write the facts about how animals stay safe. Use the information in the chart and review the selections as needed to verify their information.

		Informative/Explanatory Writing Rubric			
Score	Focus	Organization	Development of Evidence	Language and Vocabulary	Conventions
4	Main idea is clearly conveyed and well supported; response is focused.	Organization is clear and effective, creating a sense of cohesion.	Evidence is relevant and thorough; includes facts and details.	Ideas are clearly and effectively conveyed, using precise language and/or domain-specific vocabulary.	Command of conventions is strongly demonstrated.
3	Main idea is clear, adequately supported; response is generally focused.	Organization is clear, though minor flaws may be present and some ideas may be disconnected.	Evidence is adequate and includes facts and details.	Ideas are adequately conveyed, using both precise and more general language; may include domain-specific vocabulary.	Command of conventions is sufficiently demonstrated.
2	Main idea is somewhat supported; lacks focus or includes unnecessary material.	Organization is inconsistent, and flaws are apparent.	Evidence is uneven or incomplete; insufficient use of facts and details.	Ideas are unevenly conveyed, using overly-simplistic language; lacks domain-specific vocabulary.	Command of conventions is uneven.
1	Response may be confusing, unfocused; main idea insufficiently supported.	Organization is poor or nonexistent.	Evidence is poor or nonexistent.	Ideas are conveyed in a vague, unclear, or confusing manner.	There is very little command of conventions.
0	The response shows no evidence of the ability to construct a coherent explanatory essay using information from sources.				

© Common Core State Standards

Writing 2. Write informative/explanatory texts in which they name a topic, supply some facts about the topic, and provide some sense of closure.

Write Like a Reporter

Explanatory Paragraph

> **Student Prompt** Review the information about the animals in *Life in the Forest*. Write an informational report about one animal that lives in the forest. Use evidence from the selection to support your answer in your short paragraph.

_____

_____

_____

_____

_____

_____

_____

_____

_____

_____

_____

_____

Write Like a Reporter
Informative/Explanatory Paragraph

Student Prompt, p. 94 Review the information about the animals in *Life in the Forest*. Write an informational report about one animal that lives in the forest. Use evidence from the selection to support your answer in your short paragraph.

Writing to Sources Ask children to identify the animals and reread the pages that tell about each animal as they page through the selection. Ask them to choose one animal and write an informational report about the animal. Suggest that they can also look in other books and sources to find additional information. Ask children to share their writing with the group.

Children's paragraphs should:

- identify and introduce a topic
- supply supporting facts, evidence, and details about the topic
- use an effective text structure to support purpose
- demonstrate strong command of the conventions of standard written English

Ⓒ **Common Core State Standards**

Writing 2. Write informative/explanatory texts in which they name a topic, supply some facts about the topic, and provide some sense of closure.

Name_____

Connect the Texts
Explanatory Comparison

Student Prompt How are the forests in *Life in the Forest* and "A Mangrove Forest" alike? How are they different? Write sentences about each forest.

_____

_____

_____

_____

_____

_____

_____

_____

_____

_____

_____

_____

_____

_____

_____

_____

Connect the Texts
Informative/Explanatory Comparison

> **Student Prompt, p. 96** How are the forests in *Life in the Forest* and "A Mangrove Forest" alike? How are they different? Write sentences about each forest.

Writing to Sources Have children review *Life in the Forest* and "A Mangrove Forest." Review the following information with children: in both forests, the plants and the animals live together and depend on each other, and the plants and animals need one another for homes and for food. The forests are different because the forest in *Life in the Forest* doesn't have fish and the trees in "A Mangrove Forest" grow in the water. Review the information and ask children to write their reports about the likenesses and differences in the forests.

Informative/Explanatory Writing Rubric				
Score	**Focus**	**Organization**	**Development of Evidence**	**Language and Vocabulary**	**Conventions**
4	Main idea is clearly conveyed and well supported; response is focused.	Organization is clear and effective, creating a sense of cohesion.	Evidence is relevant and thorough; includes facts and details.	Ideas are clearly and effectively conveyed, using precise language and/or domain-specific vocabulary.	Command of conventions is strongly demonstrated.
3	Main idea is clear, adequately supported; response is generally focused.	Organization is clear, though minor flaws may be present and some ideas may be disconnected.	Evidence is adequate and includes facts and details.	Ideas are adequately conveyed, using both precise and more general language; may include domain-specific vocabulary.	Command of conventions is sufficiently demonstrated.
2	Main idea is somewhat supported; lacks focus or includes unnecessary material.	Organization is inconsistent, and flaws are apparent.	Evidence is uneven or incomplete; insufficient use of facts and details.	Ideas are unevenly conveyed, using overly-simplistic language; lacks domain-specific vocabulary.	Command of conventions is uneven.
1	Response may be confusing, unfocused; main idea insufficiently supported.	Organization is poor or nonexistent.	Evidence is poor or nonexistent.	Ideas are conveyed in a vague, unclear, or confusing manner.	There is very little command of conventions.
0	The response shows no evidence of the ability to construct a coherent explanatory essay using information from sources.				

© Common Core State Standards

Writing 2. Write informative/explanatory texts in which they name a topic, supply some facts about the topic, and provide some sense of closure.

Write Like a Reporter
Explanatory Paragraph

Student Prompt Look at page 178 of *Honey Bees* and read the information about expository text. Write a report about bees by telling facts about the bees. Use evidence from the selection to support your facts. End your short paragraph with a closing statement.

_____

_____

_____

_____

_____

_____

_____

_____

_____

_____

_____

_____

_____

_____

_____

_____

_____

_____

Write Like a Reporter
Informative/Explanatory Paragraph

Student Prompt, p. 98 Look at page 178 of *Honey Bees* and read the information about expository text. Write a report about bees by telling facts about the bees. Use evidence from the selection to support your facts. End your short paragraph with a closing statement.

Writing to Sources Work together with children to review the information in *Honey Bees*. Have children review the story and tell one fact about the bees. Record their facts on chart paper. Continue through the selection, concentrating on facts about bees. Review the facts and ask children to write their reports. Remind them to include a closing statement. Ask them to read their reports to the group.

Children's paragraphs should:

- introduce and focus on a topic
- support key ideas using evidence and details to support facts
- provide a sense of closure
- demonstrate strong command of the conventions of standard written English

---

Ⓒ **Common Core State Standards**

Writing 2. Write informative/explanatory texts in which they name a topic, supply some facts about the topic, and provide some sense of closure.

Name_____

Connect the Texts

Explanatory Report

> **Student Prompt** How are the insects in the poems like the bees in *Honey Bees?* Write a short report to give information about insects and bees. Tell how they are alike and different. Use details from the selections to support your ideas.

_____

_____

_____

_____

_____

_____

_____

_____

_____

_____

_____

_____

_____

_____

_____

_____

_____

Connect the Texts
Informative/Explanatory Report

Student Prompt, p. 100 How are the insects in the poems like the bees in *Honey Bees?* Write a short report to give information about insects and bees. Tell how they are alike and different. Use details from the selections to support your ideas.

Writing to Sources Review the poems and the selection *Honey Bees*. Have children find words and sentences in the texts of *Honey Bees* and the two poems to tell what the insects do. Have them tell how they are alike. Children might write about how honey bees make honey, feed their young, or build a hive. Children could tell how the insects in the poem hum at night while the bugs in the other poem live under a rock. Suggest that children can use other sources to get more information about the other insects. Ask children to share their reports with the class.

Informative/Explanatory Writing Rubric					
Score	**Focus**	**Organization**	**Development of Evidence**	**Language and Vocabulary**	**Conventions**
4	Main idea is clearly conveyed and well supported; response is focused.	Organization is clear and effective, creating a sense of cohesion.	Evidence is relevant and thorough; includes facts and details.	Ideas are clearly and effectively conveyed, using precise language and/or domain-specific vocabulary.	Command of conventions is strongly demonstrated.
3	Main idea is clear, adequately supported; response is generally focused.	Organization is clear, though minor flaws may be present and some ideas may be disconnected.	Evidence is adequate and includes facts and details.	Ideas are adequately conveyed, using both precise and more general language; may include domain-specific vocabulary.	Command of conventions is sufficiently demonstrated.
2	Main idea is somewhat supported; lacks focus or includes unnecessary material.	Organization is inconsistent, and flaws are apparent.	Evidence is uneven or incomplete; insufficient use of facts and details.	Ideas are unevenly conveyed, using overly-simplistic language; lacks domain-specific vocabulary.	Command of conventions is uneven.
1	Response may be confusing, unfocused; main idea insufficiently supported.	Organization is poor or nonexistent.	Evidence is poor or nonexistent.	Ideas are conveyed in a vague, unclear, or confusing manner.	There is very little command of conventions.
0	The response shows no evidence of the ability to construct a coherent explanatory essay using information from sources.				

Ⓒ **Common Core State Standards**

Writing 2. Write informative/explanatory texts in which they name a topic, supply some facts about the topic, and provide some sense of closure.

Prove It!
Expository Paragraph

Academic Vocabulary

In an expository paragraph, a writer writes about real people, places, or things. The writer uses facts to tell about the topic.

ELL

Introduce Genre Write *expository* on the board. Explain that this word is used for writing that is about real people, places, or things. Point out that expository text gives facts and details about the topic. It gives information to help the reader better understand the topic. Discuss with children the key features of an expository paragraph that appear on this page.

Animal Communities

Expository Paragraph

In this unit, children have read examples of informative/explanatory writing, including expository text, and have had the opportunity to write in this mode. Remind children of texts and writing tasks (such as Write Like a Reporter and Connect the Texts) in which they encountered and practiced informative/explanatory writing.

Key Features of an Expository Paragraph

- tells about real people, places, or things
- uses facts to tell about the main idea
- uses specific words to make facts clear
- develops the topic with facts, definitions, and details

Writing Task Overview

Each unit writing task provides children with an opportunity to write using information from a selection they are reading. To successfully complete the task, children must understand, interpret, and evaluate the selections and create their own response.

Animal Communities

Part 1: Children will read the selection identified from this unit. They will then respond to a question about this selection and discuss their written responses with partners or in small groups.

Part 2: Children will work individually to plan, write, and revise their own expository paragraph.

Scorable Products: evidence-based short response, expository paragraph

Animal Communities: Writing Task – Short Response

Teacher Directions:

1. Introduce the Source Reread the following selection in the Student Edition:

Life in the Forest

pp. 146–159

Explain to children that they will use the words and illustrations in the book to answer a question. Tell children that they will also write their own expository paragraph. Remind them that an expository paragraph is a paragraph about real people, places, or things. The writer uses facts to tell about the topic.

2. Have children draw a picture of the animal they chose from *Life in the Forest*.

3. Using evidence from the text, have children write or dictate an event from the selection involving the animal the children have chosen.

© **Common Core State Standards**

Writing 2. Write informative/explanatory texts in which they name a topic, supply some facts about the topic, and provide some sense of closure.

Scoring Information

Use the following 2-point scoring rubric to evaluate children's answers to the evidence-based short response questions.

Choose an animal from *Life in the Forest*. Draw a picture of the animal and write about it. Use facts and details from the selection.

	Analysis Rubric
2	The response: • demonstrates the ability to analyze facts and details about animals in the text • includes specific details that make reference to the text
1	The response: • demonstrates a limited ability to analyze facts and details about animals in the text • includes some details that make reference to the text
0	A response receives no credit if it demonstrates no ability to analyze facts and details about animals in the text or includes no relevant details from the text.

Ⓒ **Common Core State Standards**

Writing 2. Write informative/explanatory texts in which they name a topic, supply some facts about the topic, and provide some sense of closure.

Animal Communities

Writing Task – Short Response

Choose an animal from *Life in the Forest.* Draw a picture of the animal. Use facts and details from the selection.

Name _____

Write a sentence to tell about the animal.

_____
- -
_____
_____
- -
_____
_____
- -
_____
_____
- -
_____
_____
- -
_____
_____
- -
_____
_____
- -
_____
_____
- -
_____

Let's Discuss

After you have drawn your picture and written
your sentence, discuss your ideas.
Your teacher will assign you a partner or a
small group.

Animal Communities: Writing Task – Expository Paragraph

Teacher Directions:

1. Have children draw a picture of an animal community from *Life in the Forest*.

2. Have children write or dictate sentences about the animal community. Have them include information about what an animal community is and how the animals work together.

3. **Scoring Information** Use the scoring rubric on the next page to evaluate children's responses.

Ⓒ **Common Core State Standards**

Writing 2. Write informative/explanatory texts in which they name a topic, supply some facts about the topic, and provide some sense of closure.

Unit 2 **107**

		Informative/Explanatory Writing Rubric			
Score	**Focus**	**Organization**	**Development of Evidence**	**Language and Vocabulary**	**Conventions**
4	Main idea is clearly stated.	Organization is clear.	Evidence includes many facts and details.	Ideas are clearly and effectively conveyed, using precise language.	Command of conventions is strongly demonstrated.
3	Main idea is adequately stated.	Organization is clear, though minor flaws may be present.	Evidence includes some facts and details.	Ideas are adequately conveyed, using precise language.	Command of conventions is sufficiently demonstrated.
2	Main idea is somewhat stated.	Organization is inconsistent.	Evidence has insufficient use of facts or details.	Ideas are unevenly conveyed, using overly simplistic language.	Command of conventions is uneven.
1	Response may be unfocused.	Organization is poor or nonexistent.	Evidence is poor or nonexistent.	Ideas are conveyed in a vague or confusing manner.	There is very little command of conventions.
0	The response shows no evidence of the ability to construct a coherent expository paragraph using information from a source.				

© Common Core State Standards

Writing 2. Write informative/explanatory texts in which they name a topic, supply some facts about the topic, and provide some sense of closure.

Animal Communities

Writing Task – Expository Paragraph

Draw a picture that tells about an animal community.
Write sentences about the animal community.
Tell how the animals work together.

Name _____

Animal Communities: Writing Task – Expository Paragraph

Teacher Directions:

1. Publish Explain to children that publishing their writing is the last step in the writing process. If time permits, have children review one another's compositions and incorporate any comments their classmates have. Discuss different ways technology can be used to publish writing.

2. Present Children will now have the option to present their expository paragraphs. Have children give speeches about their paragraphs in front of the class. Use the list below to offer children tips on listening and speaking.

While Listening to a Classmate...

- Think about what the speaker is saying.
- Raise your hand to ask a question.

While Speaking to Classmates...

- Stay on topic.
- Speak clearly.

Things to Do Together...

- Follow agreed-upon discussion rules.
- Ask and answer questions.

© Common Core State Standards

Writing 2. Write informative/explanatory texts in which they name a topic, supply some facts about the topic, and provide some sense of closure.

Unit 3 Changes

Writing Focus: Argumentative

Name_____

Write Like a Reporter
Argument: Paragraph

Student Prompt Look at the story *A Place to Play*. Reread what Benny says on page 33. Do you agree that the place in the story is a good place for everyone? Write a short paragraph that tells your opinion. Write reasons that support your opinion. Use evidence from the text.

Write Like a Reporter

Argumentative Paragraph

> **Student Prompt, p. 114** Look at the story *A Place to Play*. Reread what Benny says on page 33. Do you agree that the place in the story is a good place for everyone? Write a short paragraph that tells your opinion. Write reasons that support your opinion. Use evidence from the text.

Writing to Sources After children review *A Place to Play*, have them turn to page 33 and reread the text. Ask children what Benny thinks of the new place in his community. (He likes it. He thinks it is a good place.) Point out that this is Benny's opinion. Ask children if they agree with Benny. What is their opinion of the new place? Help them write their opinion as a sentence: *I think the new place is _____ because _____*. Point out that they need reasons that support their opinion and they will write these reasons after the word *because*. Have children look for details in the story they can use as their reasons.

Children's paragraphs should:

- introduce the topic
- state an opinion
- supply reasons that support the opinion
- demonstrate strong command of the conventions of standard written English

© **Common Core State Standards**

Writing 1. Write opinion pieces in which they introduce the topic or name the book they are writing about, state an opinion, supply a reason for the opinion, and provide some sense of closure.

Connect the Texts

Argument: Paragraph

Student Prompt Review the neighborhoods in *A Place to Play* and "My Neighborhood, Then and Now." Which neighborhood do you like better? Write a short paragraph that tells your opinion. Look for details in the text and illustrations that support your opinion. Write these details.

_____

_____

_____

_____

_____

_____

_____

_____

_____

_____

_____

_____

_____

_____

_____

_____

_____

_____

Connect the Texts
Argumentative Paragraph

Student Prompt, p. 116 Review the neighborhoods in *A Place to Play* and "My Neighborhood, Then and Now." Which neighborhood do you like better? Write a short paragraph that tells your opinion. Look for details in the text and illustrations that support your opinion. Write these details.

Writing to Sources Have children review the text and illustrations in both selections. Ask them which neighborhood they like better and why. Point out when children say they like one thing better than another thing, they are giving their opinion. When they tell why, they are giving reasons for their opinion. Have children write their opinion and then support it using details from the selections.

	4-point Argument Writing Rubric				
Score	**Statement of Purpose/Focus**	**Organization**	**Development of Evidence**	**Language and Vocabulary**	**Conventions**
4	Opinion is clearly conveyed and well supported; response is focused.	Organization is clear and effective, creating a sense of cohesion.	Evidence is thorough and persuasive, and includes facts and details.	Ideas are clearly and effectively conveyed, using precise language and/or domain-specific vocabulary.	Command of conventions is strongly demonstrated.
3	Opinion is clear, adequately supported; response is generally focused.	Organization is clear, though minor flaws may be present and some ideas may be disconnected.	Evidence is adequate and includes facts and details.	Ideas are adequately conveyed, using both precise and more general language; may include domain-specific vocabulary.	Command of conventions is sufficiently demonstrated.
2	Opinion is somewhat supported; response may lack focus or include unnecessary material.	Organization is inconsistent, and flaws are apparent.	Evidence is uneven or incomplete; insufficient use of facts and details.	Ideas are unevenly conveyed, using overly-simplistic language; lack of domain-specific vocabulary.	Command of conventions is uneven.
1	The response may be confusing, unfocused; opinion not sufficiently supported.	Organization is poor or nonexistent.	Evidence is poor or nonexistent.	Ideas are conveyed in a vague, unclear, or confusing manner.	There is very little command of conventions.
0	The response shows no evidence of the ability to construct a coherent opinion essay using information from sources.				

ⓒ Common Core State Standards

Writing 1. Write opinion pieces in which they introduce the topic or name the book they are writing about, state an opinion, supply a reason for the opinion, and provide some sense of closure.

Write Like a Reporter

Argument: Paragraph

Student Prompt Look at page 59 in *Ruby in Her Own Time*. When the fifth egg hatches, Mother Duck and Father Duck name the duckling Ruby. Do you think Ruby is a good name for her? Write a short paragraph that tells your opinion. Include reasons that support your opinion.

_____

_____

_____

_____

_____

_____

_____

_____

_____

_____

_____

_____

_____

_____

_____

_____

Write Like a Reporter
Argumentative Paragraph

> **Student Prompt, p. 118** Look at page 59 in *Ruby in Her Own Time*. When the fifth egg hatches, Mother Duck and Father Duck name the duckling Ruby. Do you think Ruby is a good name for her? Write a short paragraph that tells your opinion. Include reasons that support your opinion.

Writing to Sources Have children review page 59 in *Ruby in Her Own Time*. Ask volunteers to give their opinion about Ruby's name. Ask them to think why they chose their response and what facts they can use to support it. Help them write their opinion as a sentence: *I think Ruby is a _____ name for her because _____.* Point out that they need reasons that support their opinion and that they will write these reasons after the word *because*. Have children look for details in the story they can use as their reasons.

Children's paragraphs should:

- state a clear opinion about the topic
- supply reasons for the opinion using details from the text to support their opinion
- provide some sense of closure by using linking words such as *because*
- demonstrate strong command of the conventions of standard written English

---

© Common Core State Standards

Writing 1. Write opinion pieces in which they introduce the topic or name the book they are writing about, state an opinion, supply a reason for the opinion, and provide some sense of closure.

Connect the Texts

Argument: Paragraph

Student Prompt *Ruby in Her Own Time* and "The Ugly Duckling" are about animals that have problems. What problem does each animal have? Which animal has the biggest problem? Write a short paragraph that tells why you chose that problem.

_____

_____

_____

_____

_____

_____

_____

_____

_____

_____

_____

_____

_____

_____

_____

_____

_____

Connect the Texts
Argumentative Paragraph

> **Student Prompt, p. 120** *Ruby in Her Own Time* and "The Ugly Duckling" are about animals that have problems. What problem does each animal have? Which animal has the biggest problem? Write a short paragraph that tells why you chose that problem.

Writing to Sources Have children review the selections *Ruby in Her Own Time* and "The Ugly Duckling" to identify the problem each animal has. Help them conclude that Ruby's problem is that she learns to do things in her own time. The ugly duckling's problem is that it looks different from the other ducklings. Have children write their opinion about the bigger problem and write their reasons they think it is bigger. Ask them to remember to include details from the selection to support their opinion. Remind children that when they say they like one thing better than another thing, they are giving their opinion. When they tell why, they are giving reasons for their opinion.

		4-point Argument Writing Rubric			
Score	Statement of Purpose/Focus	Organization	Development of Evidence	Language and Vocabulary	Conventions
4	Opinion is clearly conveyed and well supported; response is focused.	Organization is clear and effective, creating a sense of cohesion.	Evidence is thorough and persuasive, and includes facts and details.	Ideas are clearly and effectively conveyed, using precise language and/or domain-specific vocabulary.	Command of conventions is strongly demonstrated.
3	Opinion is clear, adequately supported; response is generally focused.	Organization is clear, though minor flaws may be present and some ideas may be disconnected.	Evidence is adequate and includes facts and details.	Ideas are adequately conveyed, using both precise and more general language; may include domain-specific vocabulary.	Command of conventions is sufficiently demonstrated.
2	Opinion is somewhat supported; response may lack focus or include unnecessary material.	Organization is inconsistent, and flaws are apparent.	Evidence is uneven or incomplete; insufficient use of facts and details.	Ideas are unevenly conveyed, using overly-simplistic language; lack of domain-specific vocabulary.	Command of conventions is uneven.
1	The response may be confusing, unfocused; opinion not sufficiently supported.	Organization is poor or nonexistent.	Evidence is poor or nonexistent.	Ideas are conveyed in a vague, unclear, or confusing manner.	There is very little command of conventions.
0	The response shows no evidence of the ability to construct a coherent opinion essay using information from sources.				

© Common Core State Standards

Writing 1. Write opinion pieces in which they introduce the topic or name the book they are writing about, state an opinion, supply a reason for the opinion, and provide some sense of closure.

Name _____

Write Like a Reporter

Argument: Paragraph

Student Prompt Review the story *The Class Pet*. Look at page 100. Why would the mother mouse keep the baby mice in the nest? Is this a good idea? Write your opinion. Write reasons that support your opinion. Include a closing sentence that restates your opinion.

_____

- -

_____

- -

_____

- -

_____

- -

_____

- -

_____

- -

_____

- -

_____

- -

_____

- -

_____

Write Like a Reporter

Argumentative Paragraph

Student Prompt, p. 122 Review the story *The Class Pet*. Look at page 100. Why would the mother mouse keep the baby mice in the nest? Is this a good idea? Write your opinion. Write reasons that support your opinion. Include a closing sentence that restates your opinion.

Writing to Sources After children review *The Class Pet*, have them decide whether they think keeping the baby mice in the nest is or is not a good idea. Point out that they need reasons that support their opinion and they will write these reasons. Have children look for details in the story they can use as their reasons. Then have them write their opinions. Remind children to end their writing with a closing sentence that restates their opinion. Have children share their opinions with the class.

Children's paragraphs should:

- introduce the topic
- state an opinion and supply reasons for the opinion
- provide some sense of closure by restating the opinion
- demonstrate strong command of the conventions of standard written English

Ⓒ **Common Core State Standards**

Writing 1. Write opinion pieces in which they introduce the topic or name the book they are writing about, state an opinion, supply a reason for the opinion, and provide some sense of closure.

Name_____

Connect the Texts

Argument: Paragraph

Student Prompt Think about the real mice in *The Class Pet* and the make-believe mice in "Belling the Cat." Which mice do you like best? Write your opinion. Write details from the text and illustrations to support your opinion.

_____

- -

_____

- -

_____

- -

_____

- -

_____

- -

_____

- -

_____

- -

_____

- -

_____

Connect the Texts
Argumentative Paragraph

Student Prompt, p. 124 Think about the real mice in *The Class Pet* and the make-believe mice in "Belling the Cat." Which mice do you like best? Write your opinion. Write details from the text and illustrations to support your opinion.

Writing to Sources Have children review what the mice are like in *The Class Pet* and "Belling the Cat." Ask them which mice are real and which are make-believe and give reasons for the classification. Then have children make their choice between real or make-believe mice. Remind them that when they say they like one thing better than another thing, they are giving their opinion, and when they tell why, they are giving reasons. Have children write their opinion.

4-point Argument Writing Rubric					
Score	Statement of Purpose/Focus	Organization	Development of Evidence	Language and Vocabulary	Conventions
4	Opinion is clearly conveyed and well supported; response is focused.	Organization is clear and effective, creating a sense of cohesion.	Evidence is thorough and persuasive, and includes facts and details.	Ideas are clearly and effectively conveyed, using precise language and/or domain-specific vocabulary.	Command of conventions is strongly demonstrated.
3	Opinion is clear, adequately supported; response is generally focused.	Organization is clear, though minor flaws may be present and some ideas may be disconnected.	Evidence is adequate and includes facts and details.	Ideas are adequately conveyed, using both precise and more general language; may include domain-specific vocabulary.	Command of conventions is sufficiently demonstrated.
2	Opinion is somewhat supported; response may lack focus or include unnecessary material.	Organization is inconsistent, and flaws are apparent.	Evidence is uneven or incomplete; insufficient use of facts and details.	Ideas are unevenly conveyed, using overly-simplistic language; lack of domain-specific vocabulary.	Command of conventions is uneven.
1	The response may be confusing, unfocused; opinion not sufficiently supported.	Organization is poor or nonexistent.	Evidence is poor or nonexistent.	Ideas are conveyed in a vague, unclear, or confusing manner.	There is very little command of conventions.
0	The response shows no evidence of the ability to construct a coherent opinion essay using information from sources.				

© Common Core State Standards

Writing 1. Write opinion pieces in which they introduce the topic or name the book they are writing about, state an opinion, supply a reason for the opinion, and provide some sense of closure.

Write Like a Reporter

Argument: Paragraph

Student Prompt Look at pages 133 to 137 in *Frog and Toad Together*. Reread to find out what Frog says and what Toad does. Who knows more about planting seeds? Write a short paragraph that tells why you chose Frog or Toad. Write reasons that support your opinion. Use evidence from the text.

Write Like a Reporter
Argumentative Paragraph

Student Prompt, p. 126 Look at pages 133 to 137 in *Frog and Toad Together*. Reread to find out what Frog says and what Toad does. Who knows more about planting seeds? Write a short paragraph that tells why you chose Frog or Toad. Write reasons that support your opinion. Use evidence from the text.

Writing to Sources Review *Frog and Toad Together*. Have them turn to page 133 and reread the text. Continue with the other pages to 137. Ask children to think about Frog and Toad and decide who knows more about planting seeds. Point out that they need reasons that support their opinion and they will write these reasons. Have children look for details in the story they can use as their reasons.

Children's paragraphs should:

- state a clear opinion about a topic
- supply reasons that support the opinion
- use evidence from the text to support their reasons
- demonstrate strong command of the conventions of standard written English

Ⓒ **Common Core State Standards**

Writing 1. Write opinion pieces in which they introduce the topic or name the book they are writing about, state an opinion, supply a reason for the opinion, and provide some sense of closure.

Connect the Texts

Argument: Paragraph

Student Prompt Compare the things Toad did to make a garden in *Frog and Toad Together* with the steps in "Growing Plants." Decide which selection tells an easier way to grow plants. Write a short paragraph that tells your opinion and give reasons for your choice.

_____

_____

_____

_____

_____

_____

_____

_____

_____

_____

_____

_____

_____

_____

Connect the Texts
Argumentative Paragraph

> **Student Prompt, p. 128** Compare the things Toad did to make a garden in *Frog and Toad Together* with the steps in "Growing Plants." Decide which selection tells an easier way to grow plants. Write a short paragraph that tells your opinion and give reasons for your choice.

Writing to Sources Have children find words and sentences in the text of *Frog and Toad Together* and identify what Toad did that is similar to the steps in "Growing Plants." After they compare the two texts, have them decide which selection gives the easiest instructions to plant seeds to grow plants. Have children write their opinion and then support it using details from the selections.

	4-point Argument Writing Rubric				
Score	**Statement of Purpose/Focus**	**Organization**	**Development of Evidence**	**Language and Vocabulary**	**Conventions**
4	Opinion is clearly conveyed and well supported; response is focused.	Organization is clear and effective, creating a sense of cohesion.	Evidence is thorough and persuasive, and includes facts and details.	Ideas are clearly and effectively conveyed, using precise language and/or domain-specific vocabulary.	Command of conventions is strongly demonstrated.
3	Opinion is clear, adequately supported; response is generally focused.	Organization is clear, though minor flaws may be present and some ideas may be disconnected.	Evidence is adequate and includes facts and details.	Ideas are adequately conveyed, using both precise and more general language; may include domain-specific vocabulary.	Command of conventions is sufficiently demonstrated.
2	Opinion is somewhat supported; response may lack focus or include unnecessary material.	Organization is inconsistent, and flaws are apparent.	Evidence is uneven or incomplete; insufficient use of facts and details.	Ideas are unevenly conveyed, using overly-simplistic language; lack of domain-specific vocabulary.	Command of conventions is uneven.
1	The response may be confusing, unfocused; opinion not sufficiently supported.	Organization is poor or nonexistent.	Evidence is poor or nonexistent.	Ideas are conveyed in a vague, unclear, or confusing manner.	There is very little command of conventions.
0	The response shows no evidence of the ability to construct a coherent opinion essay using information from sources.				

© **Common Core State Standards**

Writing 1. Write opinion pieces in which they introduce the topic or name the book they are writing about, state an opinion, supply a reason for the opinion, and provide some sense of closure.

Name_____

Write Like a Reporter
Argument: Paragraph

Student Prompt Reread what the caterpillar does in *I'm a Caterpillar*. Reread what the butterfly does. Which one do you think works harder? Write a short paragraph that tells your opinion. Write reasons that support your opinion. Use evidence from the text.

_____

_____

_____

_____

_____

_____

_____

_____

_____

_____

_____

_____

_____

Write Like a Reporter

Argumentative Paragraph

> **Student Prompt, p. 130** Reread what the caterpillar does in *I'm a Caterpillar*. Reread what the butterfly does. Which one do you think works harder? Write a short paragraph that tells your opinion. Write reasons that support your opinion. Use evidence from the text.

Writing to Sources After children review the caterpillar's and butterfly's activities in *I'm a Caterpillar*, make a list of them on the board. Remind them to write their opinion of which works harder and provide reasons that support their opinion. Have children look for details in the story they can use as their reasons. You may want children to work in groups to write about the opinion as a group. When the individuals or groups are finished, have them share their opinions with the class.

Children's paragraphs should:

- state a clear opinion about a topic
- provide reasons to support the opinion
- use evidence from the text to support reasons
- demonstrate strong command of the conventions of standard written English

---

Ⓒ **Common Core State Standards**

Writing 1. Write opinion pieces in which they introduce the topic or name the book they are writing about, state an opinion, supply a reason for the opinion, and provide some sense of closure.

Name_____

Connect the Texts

Argument: Paragraph

Student Prompt Review pages 172–173 of *I'm a Caterpillar* and pages 178–179 of "My Computer." Which graphic source is most helpful to you? Choose one and write your opinion in a short paragraph. Write details to support your opinion.

_____

_____

_____

_____

_____

_____

_____

_____

_____

_____

_____

_____

_____

_____

_____

Connect the Texts
Argumentative Paragraph

Student Prompt, p. 132 Review pages 172–173 of *I'm a Caterpillar* and pages 178–179 of "My Computer." Which graphic source is most helpful to you? Choose one and write your opinion in a short paragraph. Write details to support your opinion.

Writing to Sources Have children review the graphic sources in *I'm a Caterpillar* and "My Computer." Discuss what they can learn from each one and why they are used in books. Ask them to write about the graphic source they find most helpful. Point out when children say they like one thing better than another thing, they are giving their opinion. When they tell why, they are giving reasons for their opinion. Have children write their opinion.

	4-point Argument Writing Rubric				
Score	**Statement of Purpose/Focus**	**Organization**	**Development of Evidence**	**Language and Vocabulary**	**Conventions**
4	Opinion is clearly conveyed and well supported; response is focused.	Organization is clear and effective, creating a sense of cohesion.	Evidence is thorough and persuasive, and includes facts and details.	Ideas are clearly and effectively conveyed, using precise language and/or domain-specific vocabulary.	Command of conventions is strongly demonstrated.
3	Opinion is clear, adequately supported; response is generally focused.	Organization is clear, though minor flaws may be present and some ideas may be disconnected.	Evidence is adequate and includes facts and details.	Ideas are adequately conveyed, using both precise and more general language; may include domain-specific vocabulary.	Command of conventions is sufficiently demonstrated.
2	Opinion is somewhat supported; response may lack focus or include unnecessary material.	Organization is inconsistent, and flaws are apparent.	Evidence is uneven or incomplete; insufficient use of facts and details.	Ideas are unevenly conveyed, using overly-simplistic language; lack of domain-specific vocabulary.	Command of conventions is uneven.
1	The response may be confusing, unfocused; opinion not sufficiently supported.	Organization is poor or nonexistent.	Evidence is poor or nonexistent.	Ideas are conveyed in a vague, unclear, or confusing manner.	There is very little command of conventions.
0	The response shows no evidence of the ability to construct a coherent opinion essay using information from sources.				

© **Common Core State Standards**

Writing 1. Write opinion pieces in which they introduce the topic or name the book they are writing about, state an opinion, supply a reason for the opinion, and provide some sense of closure.

Name_____

Write Like a Reporter

Argument: Paragraph

Student Prompt Review the selection *Where Are My Animal Friends?* Why do some of the animals go away? Is it a good idea for them to go away? Write a short paragraph that tells your opinion. Write reasons that support your opinion. Use evidence from the text.

_____

_____

_____

_____

_____

_____

_____

_____

_____

_____

_____

_____

_____

_____

_____

_____

Write Like a Reporter
Argumentative Paragraph

Student Prompt, p. 134 Review the selection *Where Are My Animal Friends?*
Why do some of the animals go away? Is it a good idea for them to go away?
Write a short paragraph that tells your opinion. Write reasons that support your
opinion. Use evidence from the text.

Writing to Sources After children review *Where Are My Animal Friends?*, have them
turn to page 193 and reread the text. Make a list of the reasons the animals find for
going away. Then have children decide whether it is a good or bad idea to go away.
Once children choose an opinion, remind them to write their reasons to help readers
understand their choice. Have children look for details in the story they can use as
their reasons.

Children's paragraphs should:

- introduce the topic and state their opinion
- provide facts and details using text evidence to support reasons for their
  opinion
- use persuasive words to convince others their choice is best
- demonstrate strong command of the conventions of standard written English

Ⓒ **Common Core State Standards**

Writing 1. Write opinion pieces in which they introduce the topic or name the book they are writing about, state an opinion, supply a reason for the
opinion, and provide some sense of closure.

Name_____

Connect the Texts

Argument: Paragraph

> **Student Prompt** *Where Are My Animal Friends?*,
> "This Tooth," "Tommy," and "Where Do Fish Go in
> Winter?" each tell about a change. Describe each
> change. Which change do you find most interesting?
> Write a short paragraph that tells your opinion. Include
> details in the text and illustrations that support your
> opinion.

_____

_____

_____

_____

_____

_____

_____

_____

_____

_____

_____

_____

_____

_____

Connect the Texts
Argumentative Paragraph

Student Prompt, p. 136 *Where Are My Animal Friends?*, "This Tooth," "Tommy," and "Where Do Fish Go in Winter?" each tell about a change. Describe each change. Which change do you find most interesting? Write a short paragraph that tells your opinion. Include details in the text and illustrations that support your opinion.

Writing to Sources Help children review the changes in the selection and poems (*Where Are My Animal Friends?* is the animals preparing for winter, "This Tooth" is the tooth coming out, "Tommy" is a plant growing from a seed, "Where Do Fish Go in Winter?" is how the fish's behavior changes in winter). After children pick the change they find most interesting, have them write their opinion and give facts and details from the selection to help convince others that their choice is the most interesting change. Have volunteers share their opinions with the group.

4-point Argument Writing Rubric				
Score	Statement of Purpose/Focus	Organization	Development of Evidence	Language and Vocabulary	Conventions
4	Opinion is clearly conveyed and well supported; response is focused.	Organization is clear and effective, creating a sense of cohesion.	Evidence is thorough and persuasive, and includes facts and details.	Ideas are clearly and effectively conveyed, using precise language and/or domain-specific vocabulary.	Command of conventions is strongly demonstrated.
3	Opinion is clear, adequately supported; response is generally focused.	Organization is clear, though minor flaws may be present and some ideas may be disconnected.	Evidence is adequate and includes facts and details.	Ideas are adequately conveyed, using both precise and more general language; may include domain-specific vocabulary.	Command of conventions is sufficiently demonstrated.
2	Opinion is somewhat supported; response may lack focus or include unnecessary material.	Organization is inconsistent, and flaws are apparent.	Evidence is uneven or incomplete; insufficient use of facts and details.	Ideas are unevenly conveyed, using overly-simplistic language; lack of domain-specific vocabulary.	Command of conventions is uneven.
1	The response may be confusing, unfocused; opinion not sufficiently supported.	Organization is poor or nonexistent.	Evidence is poor or nonexistent.	Ideas are conveyed in a vague, unclear, or confusing manner.	There is very little command of conventions.
0	The response shows no evidence of the ability to construct a coherent opinion essay using information from sources.				

© Common Core State Standards

Writing 1. Write opinion pieces in which they introduce the topic or name the book they are writing about, state an opinion, supply a reason for the opinion, and provide some sense of closure.

Prove It!
Story Review

Academic Vocabulary

A story review is a type of argument or persuasive writing. In persuasive writing, the writer tries to persuade the reader to agree with the writer's opinion about a topic, issue, or text.

ELL

Introduce Genre Write the words *persuade* and *persuasive* on the board. Explain to children that these words describe anything that tries to convince people to think or act in a certain way. Write *review* on the board. Explain that this word means "to look at again." Tell children that a review is a type of writing in which the writer looks at something and gives an opinion about it. Discuss with children the key features of a review that appear on this page.

Making Choices

Story Review

In this unit, children have read examples of argument writing, including comments about a story, and have had the opportunity to write in this mode. Remind children of texts and writing tasks (such as Write Like a Reporter and Connect the Texts) in which they have encountered and practiced argument writing.

Key Features of a Story Review

- states the writer's opinion of a story
- supports the opinion with reasons backed by facts and details from the source
- uses persuasive words such as best, important, and should to try to convince readers to agree with the opinion
- provides a concluding statement that usually summarizes the writer's main point

Writing Task Overview

Each unit writing task provides children with an opportunity to write to a source. To successfully complete the task, children must analyze, synthesize, and evaluate a complex text and create their own written response.

Making Choices

Part 1: Children will read the selection and review the information about the selection. They can take notes or draw pictures for this source. They will then respond to several questions about this source and discuss their written responses with partners or in small groups.

Part 2: Children will work individually to plan, write, and revise their own story reviews.

Scorable Products: evidence-based short response, story review

Making Choices: Writing Task – Short Response

Teacher Directions:

1. Introduce the Source Refer children to the following text in the Student Edition:

Frog and Toad Together

pp. 126–141

Explain to children that they will need to draw evidence and support from the text above in order to answer evidence-based short response questions and to write a review. Children may draw or take notes as they closely reread the text. Children could be given paper or a relevant graphic organizer from the TR DVD for note taking.

2. Provide Directions (pp. 142–143) Answer any task-related questions children may have.

3. Facilitate Collaboration After children have completed their written responses to the evidence-based short response questions, assign partners or small groups and have them discuss their responses. If children struggle to work together productively, provide them with tips and strategies for expressing their ideas and building on others'.

© **Common Core State Standards**

Writing 1. Write opinion pieces in which they introduce the topic or name the book they are writing about, state an opinion, supply a reason for the opinion, and provide some sense of closure.

Scoring Information

Use the following 2-point scoring rubrics to evaluate children's answers to the evidence-based short response questions.

1. Look at the story. Draw pictures and write to show the characters, settings, and plot in the story. How do these story elements play a role in your response to the story?

Analysis Rubric	
2	The response: • demonstrates the ability to analyze story elements from the text • includes specific details that make reference to the text
1	The response: • demonstrates a limited ability to analyze story elements from the text • includes some details that make reference to the text
0	A response receives no credit if it demonstrates no ability to analyze story elements from the text or includes no relevant details from the text.

2. What do you think makes a good story? Give examples from the text that show how the story elements help make a good story.

Synthesis Rubric	
2	The response: • demonstrates the ability to synthesize information from the story elements in order to describe the characteristics of a good story • includes specific details that make reference to the text
1	The response: • demonstrates a limited ability to synthesize information from the story elements in order to describe the characteristics of a good story • includes some details that make reference to the text
0	A response receives no credit if it demonstrates no ability to synthesize information from the story elements or includes no relevant details from the text.

ⓒ **Common Core State Standards**

Writing 1. Write opinion pieces in which they introduce the topic or name the book they are writing about, state an opinion, supply a reason for the opinion, and provide some sense of closure.

Making Choices
Writing Task – Short Response

I. Look at the story. Draw pictures and write to show the characters, settings, and plot in the story. How do these story elements play a role in your response to the story?

Name _____

2. What do you think makes a good story? Give examples from the text that show how the story elements help make a good story.

_____

_____

_____

_____

_____

_____

_____

_____

_____

_____

_____

_____

_____

_____

_____

_____

Let's Discuss

After you have written your responses to the questions, discuss your ideas. Your teacher will assign you a partner or a small group.

Making Choices: Writing Task – Story Review

Teacher Directions:

1. **Provide Directions (p. 146)** Explain to children that they will now review their pictures or notes and plan, draft, and revise their reviews. Have children read the directions for the story review and answer any task-related questions they may have. Children should be given paper on which to write their reviews.

2. Have children write or dictate their sentences to state their opinion of the selection to write a story review.

3. **Scoring Information** Use the scoring rubric on the next page to evaluate children's story reviews.

Argument Writing Rubric

Score	Statement of Purpose/Focus	Organization	Development of Evidence	Language and Vocabulary	Conventions
4	Review clearly gives an opinion of the selection.	Organization includes a clear opinion with a strong reason.	Evidence includes sufficient facts and details.	Persuasive words are effectively used.	Use of conventions is clearly shown.
3	Review adequately gives an opinion of the selection.	Organization includes an opinion and a reason.	Evidence includes some facts and details.	Persuasive words are used.	Use of conventions is somewhat shown.
2	Review somewhat gives an opinion of the selection.	Organization includes an opinion but no reason.	Evidence does not include facts and details.	Few persuasive words are used.	Use of conventions is uneven.
1	Review does not include a stated opinion.	Organization lacks opinion, reasons, and conclusion.	Evidence is poor or nonexistent.	There is little or no use of persuasive words.	There is very little correct use of conventions.
0	The response shows no evidence of the ability to construct a coherent review using information from a source.				

Ⓒ **Common Core State Standards**

Writing 1. Write opinion pieces in which they introduce the topic or name the book they are writing about, state an opinion, supply a reason for the opinion, and provide some sense of closure.

Making Choices

Writing Task – Story Review

Story Review Prompt

Write a review of the selection. State your opinion and support it with reasons. Use examples from the selection to defend your choice.

_____
- -
_____
- -
_____
_____
- -
_____
_____
- -
_____
_____
- -
_____
_____
- -
_____
_____
- -
_____
_____
- -
_____

Making Choices: Writing Task – Story Review

Teacher Directions:

1. Publish Explain to children that publishing their writing is the last step in the writing process. If time permits, have children look at one another's compositions and incorporate any comments their classmates have. Discuss different ways technology can be used to publish writing.

2. Present Children will now have the option to present their reviews. Have children read aloud their reviews to the class. Use the list below to offer children tips on listening and speaking.

While Listening to a Classmate...
- Listen carefully.
- Think of relevant questions.

While Speaking to Classmates...
- Speak clearly at an appropriate pace.
- Face the audience.

Things to Do Together...
- Build on others' ideas.
- Ask questions to check understanding.

Ⓒ **Common Core State Standards**

Writing 1. Write opinion pieces in which they introduce the topic or name the book they are writing about, state an opinion, supply a reason for the opinion, and provide some sense of closure.

Unit 4 Treasures

Writing Focus: Informative/Explanatory

Write Like a Reporter

Explanatory Paragraph

Student Prompt Reread the selection *Mama's Birthday Present*. One of the things needed for the party is a piñata. Write a short paragraph about how it is used. Use details from the selection.

_____
_____
_____
_____
_____
_____
_____
_____
_____
_____
_____
_____
_____
_____
_____
_____
_____
_____
_____

Write Like a Reporter
Informative/Explanatory Paragraph

Student Prompt, p. 150 Reread the selection *Mama's Birthday Present*. One of the things needed for the party is a piñata. Write a short paragraph about how it is used. Use details from the selection.

Writing to Sources On the first review of *Mama's Birthday Present*, have children tell what Grandma and Francisco do to prepare for the party. Then have children review pages 36, 39, and 43 about the piñata. Have them write an article about making and using the piñata at the party.

Children's paragraphs should:
- identify and introduce a topic
- supply some facts and details about the topic using descriptive words
- provide a sense of closure
- demonstrate strong command of the conventions of standard written English

---

© **Common Core State Standards**

Writing 2. Write informative/explanatory texts in which they name a topic, supply some facts about the topic, and provide some sense of closure.

Connect the Texts

Explanatory Directions

Student Prompt Review "Limonada" and the steps to make lemonade. Why would limonada be a good thing to have at the party? Then review *Mama's Birthday Present*, where Francisco plans a birthday party for his mother. Write his plan as a set of directions. Draw a picture.

_____

_____

_____

_____

_____

_____

_____

_____

_____

_____

_____

_____

_____

_____

_____

_____

_____

_____

Connect the Texts
Informative/Explanatory Directions

Student Prompt, p. 152 Review "Limonada" and the steps to make lemonade. Why would limonada be a good thing to have at the party? Then review *Mama's Birthday Present*, where Francisco plans a birthday party for his mother. Write his plan as a set of directions. Draw a picture.

Writing to Sources Review how to write directions in "Limonada" and read the steps. Suggest that children review the selection to know what Francisco had to do. Children could write: 1. Invite guests. 2. Decide what to eat and drink. 3. Make decorations. 4. Give Mama a present.

Score	Focus	Organization	Development of Evidence	Language and Vocabulary	Conventions
Informative/Explanatory Writing Rubric					
4	Main idea is clearly conveyed and well supported; response is focused.	Organization is clear and effective, creating a sense of cohesion.	Evidence is relevant and thorough; includes facts and details.	Ideas are clearly and effectively conveyed, using precise language and/or domain-specific vocabulary.	Command of conventions is strongly demonstrated.
3	Main idea is clear, adequately supported; response is generally focused.	Organization is clear, though minor flaws may be present and some ideas may be disconnected.	Evidence is adequate and includes facts and details.	Ideas are adequately conveyed, using both precise and more general language; may include domain-specific vocabulary.	Command of conventions is sufficiently demonstrated.
2	Main idea is somewhat supported; lacks focus or includes unnecessary material.	Organization is inconsistent, and flaws are apparent.	Evidence is uneven or incomplete; insufficient use of facts and details.	Ideas are unevenly conveyed, using overly-simplistic language; lacks domain-specific vocabulary.	Command of conventions is uneven.
1	Response may be confusing, unfocused; main idea insufficiently supported.	Organization is poor or nonexistent.	Evidence is poor or nonexistent.	Ideas are conveyed in a vague, unclear, or confusing manner.	There is very little command of conventions.
0	The response shows no evidence of the ability to construct a coherent explanatory essay using information from sources.				

© Common Core State Standards

Writing 2. Write informative/explanatory texts in which they name a topic, supply some facts about the topic, and provide some sense of closure.

Write Like a Reporter

Explanatory Paragraph

Student Prompt Review *Cinderella*. Write a short descriptive paragraph about Cinderella. Tell about her and her feelings. Write a factual report based on the information in this selection.

_____

- -

_____

- -

_____

- -

_____

- -

_____

- -

_____

- -

_____

- -

_____

- -

_____

Write Like a Reporter

Informative/Explanatory Paragraph

Student Prompt, p. 154 Review *Cinderella*. Write a short descriptive paragraph about Cinderella. Tell about her and her feelings. Write a factual report based on the information in this selection.

Writing to Sources Review *Cinderella* with children. Page through the selection and have children tell things about Cinderella. Make a list of these items on chart paper. Then ask children to write a description of Cinderella telling what she does, how she acts, and what she learns. Ask children to share their descriptions.

Children's paragraphs should:

- identify and introduce a topic
- supply some facts and details about the topic
- provide a description of the topic using text evidence and illustrations
- demonstrate strong command of the conventions of standard written English

Ⓒ **Common Core State Standards**

Writing 2. Write informative/explanatory texts in which they name a topic, supply some facts about the topic, and provide some sense of closure.

Connect the Texts
Explanatory Report

> **Student Prompt** Review *Cinderella* and "Anarosa."
> What makes these two stories fairy tales? Write a
> report to tell what a fairy tale is. Use the information on
> page 82 to support your writing.

_____

_____

_____

_____

_____

_____

_____

_____

_____

_____

_____

Connect the Texts

Informative/Explanatory Report

> **Student Prompt, p. 156** Review *Cinderella* and "Anarosa." What makes these two stories fairy tales? Write a report to tell what a fairy tale is. Use the information on page 82 to support your writing.

Writing to Sources Have children review *Cinderella* and "Anarosa." Then reread the information on page 82 and discuss the features of a fairy tale. Then have them write a report to explain what a fairy tale is. Suggest that they include items from *Cinderella* and "Anarosa" to support their information.

			Informative/Explanatory Writing Rubric		
Score	**Focus**	**Organization**	**Development of Evidence**	**Language and Vocabulary**	**Conventions**
4	Main idea is clearly conveyed and well supported; response is focused.	Organization is clear and effective, creating a sense of cohesion.	Evidence is relevant and thorough; includes facts and details.	Ideas are clearly and effectively conveyed, using precise language and/or domain-specific vocabulary.	Command of conventions is strongly demonstrated.
3	Main idea is clear, adequately supported; response is generally focused.	Organization is clear, though minor flaws may be present and some ideas may be disconnected.	Evidence is adequate and includes facts and details.	Ideas are adequately conveyed, using both precise and more general language; may include domain-specific vocabulary.	Command of conventions is sufficiently demonstrated.
2	Main idea is somewhat supported; lacks focus or includes unnecessary material.	Organization is inconsistent, and flaws are apparent.	Evidence is uneven or incomplete; insufficient use of facts and details.	Ideas are unevenly conveyed, using overly-simplistic language; lacks domain-specific vocabulary.	Command of conventions is uneven.
1	Response may be confusing, unfocused; main idea insufficiently supported.	Organization is poor or nonexistent.	Evidence is poor or nonexistent.	Ideas are conveyed in a vague, unclear, or confusing manner.	There is very little command of conventions.
0	The response shows no evidence of the ability to construct a coherent explanatory essay using information from sources.				

© Common Core State Standards

Writing 2. Write informative/explanatory texts in which they name a topic, supply some facts about the topic, and provide some sense of closure.

Write Like a Reporter
Explanatory Paragraph

Student Prompt Look at the selection, *A Trip to Washington, D.C.* Write a short paragraph about one thing you can see in Washington, D.C. Be sure to include specific facts and details about that place.

_____

- -

_____

- -

_____

- -

_____

- -

_____

- -

_____

- -

_____

- -

_____

- -

_____

Write Like a Reporter
Informative/Explanatory Paragraph

Student Prompt, p. 158 Look at the selection, *A Trip to Washington, D.C.* Write a short paragraph about one thing you can see in Washington, D.C. Be sure to include specific facts and details about that place.

Writing to Sources Ask children to identify the places shown in *A Trip to Washington, D.C.* Ask children to choose one of the places and write about it. Point out that they should use details in the words and pictures to tell about the place they chose. Children may also do some research in books or online sources to find more information.

Children's paragraphs should:

- identify and introduce a topic
- supply some facts and details about the topic using text evidence and photographs
- provide a sense of closure
- demonstrate strong command of the conventions of standard written English

Ⓒ **Common Core State Standards**

Writing 2. Write informative/explanatory texts in which they name a topic, supply some facts about the topic, and provide some sense of closure.

Connect the Texts

Explanatory Paragraph

Student Prompt *A Trip to Washington, D.C.* and "My 4th of July" tell about things that are important to Americans. Choose one item and write a paragraph about why it is important to Americans.

_____

_____

_____

_____

_____

_____

_____

_____

_____

_____

_____

_____

_____

_____

_____

_____

_____

_____

Connect the Texts

Informative/Explanatory Paragraph

Student Prompt, p. 160 *A Trip to Washington, D.C.* and "My 4th of July" tell about things that are important to Americans. Choose one item and write a paragraph about why it is important to Americans.

Writing to Sources Have children review *A Trip to Washington, D.C.* and "My 4th of July." Ask them to choose one place or event in the selection and write to tell why it is important to Americans. Have them use the information in the text and other sources (books and online information) to add to their explanation.

			Informative/Explanatory Writing Rubric		
Score	**Focus**	**Organization**	**Development of Evidence**	**Language and Vocabulary**	**Conventions**
4	Main idea is clearly conveyed and well supported; response is focused.	Organization is clear and effective, creating a sense of cohesion.	Evidence is relevant and thorough; includes facts and details.	Ideas are clearly and effectively conveyed, using precise language and/or domain-specific vocabulary.	Command of conventions is strongly demonstrated.
3	Main idea is clear, adequately supported; response is generally focused.	Organization is clear, though minor flaws may be present and some ideas may be disconnected.	Evidence is adequate and includes facts and details.	Ideas are adequately conveyed, using both precise and more general language; may include domain-specific vocabulary.	Command of conventions is sufficiently demonstrated.
2	Main idea is somewhat supported; lacks focus or includes unnecessary material.	Organization is inconsistent, and flaws are apparent.	Evidence is uneven or incomplete; insufficient use of facts and details.	Ideas are unevenly conveyed, using overly-simplistic language; lacks domain-specific vocabulary.	Command of conventions is uneven.
1	Response may be confusing, unfocused; main idea insufficiently supported.	Organization is poor or nonexistent.	Evidence is poor or nonexistent.	Ideas are conveyed in a vague, unclear, or confusing manner.	There is very little command of conventions.
0	The response shows no evidence of the ability to construct a coherent explanatory essay using information from sources.				

© Common Core State Standards

Writing 2. Write informative/explanatory texts in which they name a topic, supply some facts about the topic, and provide some sense of closure.

Write Like a Reporter
Explanatory Paragraph

Student Prompt Reread *A Southern Ranch*. Write a report that tells how ranch hands keep the herd together. Use text evidence and photographs from the selection to support your writing.

_____

_____

_____

_____

_____

_____

_____

_____

_____

_____

_____

_____

_____

_____

_____

Write Like a Reporter

Informative/Explanatory Paragraph

Student Prompt, p. 162 Reread *A Southern Ranch*. Write a report that tells how ranch hands keep the herd together. Use text evidence and photographs from the selection to support your writing.

Writing to Sources Review the selection with children and discuss details from the photographs. Have children use the text and photographs to write a report telling how ranch hands control their herd. Suggest that children do some research in books or online sources to find more information.

Children's paragraphs should:

- identify and introduce main idea
- supply some facts and details about the topic using text evidence and photographs
- provide a sense of closure
- demonstrate strong command of the conventions of standard written English

Ⓒ **Common Core State Standards**

Writing 2. Write informative/explanatory texts in which they name a topic, supply some facts about the topic, and provide some sense of closure.

Connect the Texts

Explanatory Paragraph

Student Prompt Think about the information in the two selections. Why is it a good idea to have signs near a ranch? Write a one-paragraph explanation telling why the signs on pages 150–151 are important. Use the information on page 148 for support.

_____

_____

_____

_____

_____

_____

_____

_____

_____

_____

Connect the Texts
Informative/Explanatory Paragraph

> **Student Prompt, p. 164** Think about the information in the two selections. Why is it a good idea to have signs near a ranch? Write a one-paragraph explanation telling why the signs on pages 150–151 are important. Use the information on page 148 for support.

Writing to Sources Review *A Southern Ranch* and "On the Way to a Ranch" with children. Discuss why signs near and on a ranch can be helpful. Have children look at the signs on pages 150–151 and write about why these signs are important. Tell them to use the information on page 148 to support their explanations.

Score	Focus	Organization	Development of Evidence	Language and Vocabulary	Conventions
Informative/Explanatory Writing Rubric					
4	Main idea is clearly conveyed and well supported; response is focused.	Organization is clear and effective, creating a sense of cohesion.	Evidence is relevant and thorough; includes facts and details.	Ideas are clearly and effectively conveyed, using precise language and/or domain-specific vocabulary.	Command of conventions is strongly demonstrated.
3	Main idea is clear, adequately supported; response is generally focused.	Organization is clear, though minor flaws may be present and some ideas may be disconnected.	Evidence is adequate and includes facts and details.	Ideas are adequately conveyed, using both precise and more general language; may include domain-specific vocabulary.	Command of conventions is sufficiently demonstrated.
2	Main idea is somewhat supported; lacks focus or includes unnecessary material.	Organization is inconsistent, and flaws are apparent.	Evidence is uneven or incomplete; insufficient use of facts and details.	Ideas are unevenly conveyed, using overly-simplistic language; lacks domain-specific vocabulary.	Command of conventions is uneven.
1	Response may be confusing, unfocused; main idea insufficiently supported.	Organization is poor or nonexistent.	Evidence is poor or nonexistent.	Ideas are conveyed in a vague, unclear, or confusing manner.	There is very little command of conventions.
0	The response shows no evidence of the ability to construct a coherent explanatory essay using information from sources.				

© Common Core State Standards

Writing 2. Write informative/explanatory texts in which they name a topic, supply some facts about the topic, and provide some sense of closure.

Write Like a Reporter

Explanatory Paragraph

Student Prompt Review pages 168–169 of *Peter's Chair.* Write a one-paragraph explanation telling why Peter takes his chair to his room. Use evidence to support your writing.

_____

- -

_____

- -

_____

- -

_____

- -

_____

- -

_____

- -

_____

- -

_____

- -

_____

Write Like a Reporter
Informative/Explanatory Paragraph

Student Prompt, p. 166 Review pages 168–169 of *Peter's Chair.* Write a one-paragraph explanation telling why Peter takes his chair to his room. Use evidence to support your writing.

Writing to Sources Review the selection with children. Discuss the text and illustrations. How is Peter feeling? Have children write an explanation telling why Peter takes his chair to his room. Remind them to use evidence from the text to support their explanation.

Children's paragraphs should:
- identify and introduce key idea
- supply some facts and details that support conclusions
- provide a sense of closure
- demonstrate strong command of the conventions of standard written English

Ⓒ **Common Core State Standards**

Writing 2. Write informative/explanatory texts in which they name a topic, supply some facts about the topic, and provide some sense of closure.

Connect the Texts
Explanatory E-mail

Student Prompt Reread *Peter's Chair* and "Peter's Baby Sister." Peter's chair is very special to him. Using evidence from the text, write an e-mail that explains why the chair is special to him.

_____

_____

_____

_____

_____

_____

_____

_____

_____

_____

_____

_____

_____

_____

_____

_____

Connect the Texts
Informative/Explanatory E-mail

Student Prompt, p. 168 Reread *Peter's Chair* and "Peter's Baby Sister." Peter's chair is very special to him. Using evidence from the text, write an e-mail that explains why the chair is special to him.

Writing to Sources Review the two selections with children. Discuss why Peter's chair is special to him. Have them write an e-mail to a friend explaining why the chair is special to Peter. Tell children to structure their e-mails just like the e-mail in "Peter's Baby Sister."

Score	Focus	Organization	Development of Evidence	Language and Vocabulary	Conventions
Informative/Explanatory Writing Rubric					
4	Main idea is clearly conveyed and well supported; response is focused.	Organization is clear and effective, creating a sense of cohesion.	Evidence is relevant and thorough; includes facts and details.	Ideas are clearly and effectively conveyed, using precise language and/or domain-specific vocabulary.	Command of conventions is strongly demonstrated.
3	Main idea is clear, adequately supported; response is generally focused.	Organization is clear, though minor flaws may be present and some ideas may be disconnected.	Evidence is adequate and includes facts and details.	Ideas are adequately conveyed, using both precise and more general language; may include domain-specific vocabulary.	Command of conventions is sufficiently demonstrated.
2	Main idea is somewhat supported; lacks focus or includes unnecessary material.	Organization is inconsistent, and flaws are apparent.	Evidence is uneven or incomplete; insufficient use of facts and details.	Ideas are unevenly conveyed, using overly-simplistic language; lacks domain-specific vocabulary.	Command of conventions is uneven.
1	Response may be confusing, unfocused; main idea insufficiently supported.	Organization is poor or nonexistent.	Evidence is poor or nonexistent.	Ideas are conveyed in a vague, unclear, or confusing manner.	There is very little command of conventions.
0	The response shows no evidence of the ability to construct a coherent explanatory essay using information from sources.				

Ⓒ Common Core State Standards

Writing 2. Write informative/explanatory texts in which they name a topic, supply some facts about the topic, and provide some sense of closure.

Name_____

Write Like a Reporter
Explanatory Paragraph

Student Prompt Reread pages 212–216 of *Henry and Mudge and Mrs. Hopper's House.* Write a short paragraph that tells about the different costumes that Henry and Mudge try on. Use evidence from the text and illustrations as you write.

_____
_____
_____
_____
_____
_____
_____
_____
_____
_____
_____
_____
_____
_____
_____
_____
_____
_____

Write Like a Reporter
Informative/Explanatory Paragraph

Student Prompt, p. 170 Reread pages 212–216 of *Henry and Mudge and Mrs. Hopper's House.* Write a short paragraph that tells about the different costumes that Henry and Mudge try on. Use evidence from the text and illustrations as you write.

Writing to Sources Review the selection with children. Discuss the text and illustrations on pages 212–216. Have children identify the different costumes that Henry and Mudge try on. Then have them write a descriptive report about the costumes. Remind them to use details from the text to support their writing.

Children's paragraphs should:
- identify and introduce a topic
- supply some facts and details about the topic using illustrations and descriptive words
- provide a sense of closure
- demonstrate strong command of the conventions of standard written English

Ⓒ **Common Core State Standards**

Writing 2. Write informative/explanatory texts in which they name a topic, supply some facts about the topic, and provide some sense of closure.

Connect the Texts
Explanatory Paragraph

Student Prompt Reread *Henry and Mudge and Mrs. Hopper's House* and the poetry collection. How are the treasures in *Henry and Mudge and Mrs. Hopper's House* and the treasures in the poems alike and different? Write a short paragraph that compares and contrasts the treasures. Cite evidence from the text and the illustrations.

_____

_____

_____

_____

_____

_____

_____

_____

_____

_____

_____

_____

_____

Connect the Texts
Informative/Explanatory Paragraph

Student Prompt, p. 172 Reread *Henry and Mudge and Mrs. Hopper's House* and the poetry collection. How are the treasures in *Henry and Mudge and Mrs. Hopper's House* and the treasures in the poems alike and different? Write a short paragraph that compares and contrasts the treasures. Cite evidence from the text and the illustrations.

Writing to Sources Review *Henry and Mudge and Mrs. Hopper's House* and the poetry collection with children. Discuss the items in the story and the poems that are considered treasures. Make a T-chart with children that compares and contrasts the treasures. Then have them write about how the treasures are alike and different. Remind children to use details to support their writing.

Informative/Explanatory Writing Rubric					
Score	Focus	Organization	Development of Evidence	Language and Vocabulary	Conventions
4	Main idea is clearly conveyed and well supported; response is focused.	Organization is clear and effective, creating a sense of cohesion.	Evidence is relevant and thorough; includes facts and details.	Ideas are clearly and effectively conveyed, using precise language and/or domain-specific vocabulary.	Command of conventions is strongly demonstrated.
3	Main idea is clear, adequately supported; response is generally focused.	Organization is clear, though minor flaws may be present and some ideas may be disconnected.	Evidence is adequate and includes facts and details.	Ideas are adequately conveyed, using both precise and more general language; may include domain-specific vocabulary.	Command of conventions is sufficiently demonstrated.
2	Main idea is somewhat supported; lacks focus or includes unnecessary material.	Organization is inconsistent, and flaws are apparent.	Evidence is uneven or incomplete; insufficient use of facts and details.	Ideas are unevenly conveyed, using overly-simplistic language; lacks domain-specific vocabulary.	Command of conventions is uneven.
1	Response may be confusing, unfocused; main idea insufficiently supported.	Organization is poor or nonexistent.	Evidence is poor or nonexistent.	Ideas are conveyed in a vague, unclear, or confusing manner.	There is very little command of conventions.
0	The response shows no evidence of the ability to construct a coherent explanatory essay using information from sources.				

Ⓒ Common Core State Standards

Writing 2. Write informative/explanatory texts in which they name a topic, supply some facts about the topic, and provide some sense of closure.

Prove It!
Research Report

Academic Vocabulary

A report is an article that shares information about someone or something. It supplies facts and details gathered from sources.

ELL

Introduce Genre Write *research report* on the board. Explain that *research report* describes a kind of writing that teaches the reader about a topic. Tell children that the information from a research report comes from outside sources. These sources may include Web sites, books, and articles. Discuss with children the key features of a research report that appear on this page.

Do the Research

Research Report
In this unit, children have read examples of informative/ explanatory writing and have had the opportunity to write in this mode. Remind children of texts and writing tasks (such as Write Like a Reporter and Connect the Texts) in which they encountered informative/explanatory writing.

Key Features of a Research Report
- tells about real people, places, or things
- uses details to tell about the topic
- provides facts from sources such as books and Web sites
- presents information and ideas in an order that makes sense

Writing Task Overview

Each unit writing task provides children with an opportunity to write to sources. To successfully complete the task, children must analyze, synthesize, and evaluate the specified texts and create their own written response.

Do the Research

Part 1: Children will reread the selections identified from this unit. They will then respond to several questions about these sources and discuss their written responses with partners.

Part 2: Children will work individually to plan, write, and revise their own research report in which they supply information about something they see in a photograph in one of the selections.

Scorable Products: evidence-based short response, research report

Do the Research: Writing Task – Short Response

Teacher Directions:

1. Introduce the Sources Refer children to the following texts in the Student Edition:

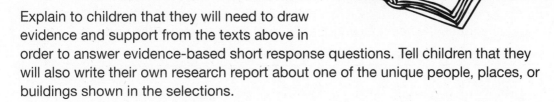

1. *A Trip to Washington, D.C.,* pp. 96–109

2. *A Southern Ranch,* pp. 128–143

Explain to children that they will need to draw evidence and support from the texts above in order to answer evidence-based short response questions. Tell children that they will also write their own research report about one of the unique people, places, or buildings shown in the selections.

2. Provide Directions (pp. 178–179) Answer any task-related questions children may have.

3. Facilitate Collaboration After children have completed their written responses to the evidence-based short response questions, assign small groups and have them discuss their responses. If children struggle to work together productively, provide them with tips and·strategies for expressing their ideas and building on others'.

ⓒ **Common Core State Standards**

Writing 2. Write informative/explanatory texts in which they name a topic, supply some facts about the topic, and provide some sense of closure.

Scoring Information

Use the following 2-point scoring rubrics to evaluate children's answers to the evidence-based short response questions.

1. Look at each selection. Draw a picture of something from the selections you would like to see in person. What makes that place special?

	Analysis Rubric
2	The response: • demonstrates the ability to analyze different images across the texts • includes specific details that make reference to the texts
1	The response: • demonstrates a limited ability to analyze different images across the texts • includes some details that make reference to the texts
0	A response receives no credit if it demonstrates no ability to analyze different images across the texts or includes no relevant details from the texts.

2. Both Washington, D.C., and a southern ranch are interesting places to visit. How are these places different from where you live? How are they similar? What more would you like to learn about them?

	Synthesis Rubric	
2	The response: • demonstrates the ability to synthesize information from the sources in order to describe how each location is alike/different from where they live • includes specific details that make reference to the texts	
1	The response: • demonstrates a limited ability to synthesize information from the sources in order to describe how each location is alike/different from where they live • includes some details that make reference to the texts	
0	A response receives no credit if it demonstrates no ability to synthesize information from the sources or includes no relevant details from the texts.	

© Common Core State Standards

Writing 2. Write informative/explanatory texts in which they name a topic, supply some facts about the topic, and provide some sense of closure.

Unit 4   **177**

Name _____

Do the Research

Writing Task – Short Response

I. Look at each selection. Draw a picture of something from the selections you would like to see in person. What makes that place special? Write about it.

Name _____

2. Both Washington, D.C., and a southern ranch are interesting places to visit. How are these places different from where you live? How are they similar? What more would you like to learn about them?

_____

_____

_____

_____

_____

_____

_____

_____

_____

_____

_____

_____

_____

_____

_____

_____

Let's Discuss

After you have written your responses to the questions, discuss your ideas. Your teacher will assign you a partner or a small group.

Do the Research: Writing Task – Research Report

Teacher Directions:

1. **Provide Directions (p. 182)** Explain to children that they will now review the sources and plan, draft, and revise their research reports. Although they may use the sources, they must work alone. Children will be allowed to look back at the answers they wrote to the short response questions, but they are not allowed to make changes to those answers. Have children read the directions for the research report and answer any task-related questions they may have. Children should be given paper on which to write their research report.

2. **Scoring Information** Use the scoring rubric on the next page to evaluate children's research reports.

3. **Research Report Prompt** Write a research report about a photo from one of the selections that you want to learn more about. What makes the person, place, or buildings shown so special? Use details from the selection to support your points. Also use additional books and Web sites to find out more information about your topic.

Informative/Explanatory Writing Rubric

Score	Focus	Organization	Development of Evidence	Language and Vocabulary	Conventions
4	Main idea is clearly stated.	Organization is clear and effective.	Evidence includes many facts and details.	Ideas are clearly and effectively included, using precise language.	Command of conventions is strongly demonstrated.
3	Main idea is adequately stated.	Organization is clear, though minor flaws may be present.	Evidence includes some facts and details.	Ideas are adequately included, using precise language.	Command of conventions is sufficiently demonstrated.
2	Main idea is somewhat stated.	Organization is inconsistent.	Evidence has insufficient use of facts or details.	Ideas are unevenly included, using overly-simplistic language.	Command of conventions is uneven.
1	Response may be confusing, unfocused.	Organization is poor or nonexistent.	Evidence is poor or nonexistent.	Ideas are included in a vague or confusing manner.	There is very little command of conventions.
0	The response shows no evidence of the ability to construct a coherent expository paragraph using information from sources.				

Ⓒ Common Core State Standards

Writing 2. Write informative/explanatory texts in which they name a topic, supply some facts about the topic, and provide some sense of closure.

Name _____

Do the Research

Writing Task – Research Report

Research Report Prompt

Write a research report about a photo from one of the selections that you want to learn more about. What makes the person, place, or buildings shown so special? Use details from the selection to support your points. Also use additional books and Web sites to find out more information about your topic.

_____

_____

_____

_____

_____

_____

_____

_____

_____

_____

_____

_____

_____

_____

_____

_____

_____

_____

_____

Do the Research: Writing Task – Research Report

Teacher Directions:

1. Publish Explain to children that publishing their writing is the last step in the writing process. If time permits, have children review one another's compositions and incorporate any comments their classmates have. Discuss different ways technology can be used to publish writing.

2. Present Children will now have the option to present their research reports. Have children read their reports aloud in front of the class. Use the list below to offer children tips on listening and speaking.

While Listening to a Classmate...
- Think about what the speaker is saying.
- Raise your hand to ask a question.

While Speaking to Classmates...
- Stay on topic.
- Speak clearly.

Things to Do Together...
- Follow agreed-upon discussion rules.
- Ask and answer questions.

Ⓒ **Common Core State Standards**

Writing 2. Write informative/explanatory texts in which they name a topic, supply some facts about the topic, and provide some sense of closure.

Unit 5 Great Ideas

Writing Focus: Argumentative

Name_____

Write Like a Reporter

Argument: Paragraph

Student Prompt Reread *Tippy-Toe Chick, Go!* Notice what happens to Dog on page 36. Do you think Little Chick used a good plan to reach the garden? Write a short paragraph that tells your opinion. Support your opinion with reasons. Use evidence from the text.

_____

_____

_____

_____

_____

_____

_____

_____

_____

_____

_____

_____

_____

_____

_____

_____

Write Like a Reporter
Argumentative Paragraph

Student Prompt, p. 186 Reread *Tippy-Toe Chick, Go!* Notice what happens to Dog on page 36. Do you think Little Chick used a good plan to reach the garden? Write a short paragraph that tells your opinion. Support your opinion with reasons. Use evidence from the text.

Writing to Sources After children review *Tippy-Toe Chick, Go!*, have them turn to pages 32–33 and look at the illustration. Ask children how Dog looks. Have them think about how Dog reacted when the other chicks tried to get him to cooperate. Ask volunteers to share their opinion of Little Chick's plan. Help them write their opinion as a sentence: *I think Little Chick's plan was _____ because _____.* Point out that they need reasons that support their opinion and they will write these reasons after the word *because*. Have children locate details in the story to use as their reasons.

Children's paragraphs should:

- introduce the topic
- state an opinion
- supply a reason for that opinion
- demonstrate strong command of the conventions of standard written English

---

© **Common Core State Standards**

Writing 1. Write opinion pieces in which they introduce the topic or name the book they are writing about, state an opinion, supply a reason for the opinion, and provide some sense of closure.

Connect the Texts

Argument: Paragraph

Student Prompt Think about Little Chick in *Tippy-Toe Chick, Go!* and Little Red Hen in "Little Red Hen." Do you think Little Red Hen would ask Little Chick for help? Do you think Little Chick would say yes? Write a short paragraph that tells your opinion. Look for details in the text that support your opinion. Write these details.

_____

_____

_____

_____

_____

_____

_____

_____

_____

_____

_____

_____

_____

Connect the Texts
Argumentative Paragraph

> **Student Prompt, p. 188** Think about Little Chick in *Tippy-Toe Chick, Go!*
> and Little Red Hen in "Little Red Hen." Do you think Little Red Hen would ask
> Little Chick for help? Do you think Little Chick would say yes? Write a short
> paragraph that tells your opinion. Look for details in the text that support your
> opinion. Write these details.

Writing to Sources Have children review the text in both selections. Ask children to
turn to page 30 of *Tippy-Toe Chick, Go!* Prompt them to think about what they know
about Little Chick from this text. Guide children in understanding that Little Red Hen
asks for help from several different animals. Then have children write their opinion
and support it using details from the selections.

		4-point Argument Writing Rubric			
Score	**Statement of Purpose/Focus**	**Organization**	**Development of Evidence**	**Language and Vocabulary**	**Conventions**
4	Opinion is clearly conveyed and well supported; response is focused.	Organization is clear and effective, creating a sense of cohesion.	Evidence is thorough and persuasive, and includes facts and details.	Ideas are clearly and effectively conveyed, using precise language and/or domain-specific vocabulary.	Command of conventions is strongly demonstrated.
3	Opinion is clear, adequately supported; response is generally focused.	Organization is clear, though minor flaws may be present and some ideas may be disconnected.	Evidence is adequate and includes facts and details.	Ideas are adequately conveyed, using both precise and more general language; may include domain-specific vocabulary.	Command of conventions is sufficiently demonstrated.
2	Opinion is somewhat supported; response may lack focus or include unnecessary material.	Organization is inconsistent, and flaws are apparent.	Evidence is uneven or incomplete; insufficient use of facts and details.	Ideas are unevenly conveyed, using overly-simplistic language; lack of domain-specific vocabulary.	Command of conventions is uneven.
1	The response may be confusing, unfocused; opinion not sufficiently supported.	Organization is poor or nonexistent.	Evidence is poor or nonexistent.	Ideas are conveyed in a vague, unclear, or confusing manner.	There is very little command of conventions.
0	The response shows no evidence of the ability to construct a coherent opinion essay using information from sources.				

© **Common Core State Standards**

Writing 1. Write opinion pieces in which they introduce the topic or name the book they are writing about, state an opinion, supply a reason for the opinion, and provide some sense of closure.

Write Like a Reporter

Argument: Paragraph

Student Prompt Look at pages 76–77 in *Mole and the Baby Bird*. Do you think Mole made the right choice when he let his bird go free? Write a short paragraph that tells your opinion about Mole's idea. Support your opinion with evidence from the text.

_____

_____

_____

_____

_____

_____

_____

_____

_____

_____

_____

_____

_____

_____

Write Like a Reporter
Argumentative Paragraph

Student Prompt, p. 190 Look at pages 76–77 in *Mole and the Baby Bird*. Do you think Mole made the right choice when he let his bird go free? Write a short paragraph that tells your opinion about Mole's idea. Support your opinion with evidence from the text.

Writing to Sources Have children review page 75 of *Mole and the Baby Bird*. Invite volunteers to give their opinion about Mole's decision to free his bird. Ask them to consider why they chose their response. Have them think about the text evidence that supports this opinion. Help them write their opinion as a sentence: *I think Mole made the _____ choice because _____*. Explain that children will write either *right* or *wrong* on the first line. Point out that they need reasons that support their opinion and they will write these reasons after the word *because*. Have children locate details in the story to use as their reasons.

Children's paragraphs should:
- introduce the topic
- clearly state an opinion
- supply a reason for the opinion
- demonstrate strong command of the conventions of standard written English

Ⓒ Common Core State Standards

Writing 1. Write opinion pieces in which they introduce the topic or name the book they are writing about, state an opinion, supply a reason for the opinion, and provide some sense of closure.

Connect the Texts

Argument: Paragraph

Student Prompt *Mole and the Baby Bird* and "Brave Little Cuckoo" are about animals that help others. Who do you think was more helpful? Write a short paragraph that tells your opinion. Use details from both stories to support your opinion.

_____

_____

_____

_____

_____

_____

_____

_____

_____

_____

_____

_____

_____

_____

_____

_____

_____

_____

Connect the Texts

Argumentative Paragraph

Student Prompt, p. 192 *Mole and the Baby Bird* and "Brave Little Cuckoo" are about animals that help others. Who do you think was more helpful? Write a short paragraph that tells your opinion. Use details from both stories to support your opinion.

Writing to Sources Have children reread *Mole and the Baby Bird* and "Brave Little Cuckoo" to review how the main character of each selection helps others. Help them identify that Mole cares for a small bird that had fallen out of its nest. Cuckoo helps the other forest animals by saving their seeds from a fire. Have children write their opinion about whether Mole or Cuckoo was more helpful. Remind them to include details from each selection to support their opinion. Explain to children that when they say one animal is more helpful than another, they are giving their opinion. When they use details in the text to tell why, they are supporting their opinion.

	4-point Argument Writing Rubric				
Score	**Statement of Purpose/Focus**	**Organization**	**Development of Evidence**	**Language and Vocabulary**	**Conventions**
4	Opinion is clearly conveyed and well supported; response is focused.	Organization is clear and effective, creating a sense of cohesion.	Evidence is thorough and persuasive, and includes facts and details.	Ideas are clearly and effectively conveyed, using precise language and/or domain-specific vocabulary.	Command of conventions is strongly demonstrated.
3	Opinion is clear, adequately supported; response is generally focused.	Organization is clear, though minor flaws may be present and some ideas may be disconnected.	Evidence is adequate and includes facts and details.	Ideas are adequately conveyed, using both precise and more general language; may include domain-specific vocabulary.	Command of conventions is sufficiently demonstrated.
2	Opinion is somewhat supported; response may lack focus or include unnecessary material.	Organization is inconsistent, and flaws are apparent.	Evidence is uneven or incomplete; insufficient use of facts and details.	Ideas are unevenly conveyed, using overly-simplistic language; lack of domain-specific vocabulary.	Command of conventions is uneven.
1	The response may be confusing, unfocused; opinion not sufficiently supported.	Organization is poor or nonexistent.	Evidence is poor or nonexistent.	Ideas are conveyed in a vague, unclear, or confusing manner.	There is very little command of conventions.
0	The response shows no evidence of the ability to construct a coherent opinion essay using information from sources.				

© Common Core State Standards

Writing 1. Write opinion pieces in which they introduce the topic or name the book they are writing about, state an opinion, supply a reason for the opinion, and provide some sense of closure.

Write Like a Reporter

Argument: Paragraph

Student Prompt Reread *Dot & Jabber and the Great Acorn Mystery*. Who do you think is a better detective, Dot or Jabber? Write a short paragraph that tells your opinion. Include reasons from the illustrations and text that support your opinion.

Write Like a Reporter
Argumentative Paragraph

> **Student Prompt, p. 194** Reread *Dot & Jabber and the Great Acorn Mystery*.
> Who do you think is a better detective, Dot or Jabber? Write a short paragraph
> that tells your opinion. Include reasons from the illustrations and text that
> support your opinion.

Writing to Sources Have children review *Dot & Jabber and the Great Acorn
Mystery* and have them think about what each character says and does. Have them
decide which mouse is a better detective. Have children find details in the story they
can use as evidence to support their opinion. Then have them write their opinion.
Encourage children to use persuasive words in their opinion pieces, such as *better*
or *best*.

Children's paragraphs should:

- introduce the topic
- state an opinion clearly
- supply a strong reason for the opinion
- include a persuasive word, such as *better*
- demonstrate strong command of the conventions of standard written English

© **Common Core State Standards**

Writing 1. Write opinion pieces in which they introduce the topic or name the book they are writing about, state an opinion, supply a reason for the
opinion, and provide some sense of closure.

Name_____

Connect the Texts

Argument: Paragraph

Student Prompt *Dot & Jabber and the Great Acorn Mystery* and "Water" are about answering questions. Dot and Jabber find answers by exploring. The children in "Water" run tests in the classroom. Which do you think is a better way to find answers? Write a short paragraph that tells your opinion. Use details from the text and images of both selections to support your opinion.

_____

- -

_____

- -

_____

- -

_____

- -

_____

- -

_____

- -

_____

- -

_____

- -

_____

- -

_____

Connect the Texts
Argumentative Paragraph

Student Prompt, p. 196 *Dot & Jabber and the Great Acorn Mystery* and "Water" are about answering questions. Dot and Jabber find answers by exploring. The children in "Water" run tests in the classroom. Which do you think is a better way to find answers? Write a short paragraph that tells your opinion. Use details from the text and images of both selections to support your opinion.

Writing to Sources Have children review *Dot & Jabber and the Great Acorn Mystery* and "Water." Encourage them to think about the advantages and disadvantages of finding answers through exploration versus classroom investigations. Then have children make their choice about the better way to find answers. Remind them that when they say something is better than something else, they are giving their opinion. When they tell why, they are giving reasons. Have children write their opinion, using evidence from both texts as support. Have volunteers share their opinions with the class.

	4-point Argument Writing Rubric				
Score	**Statement of Purpose/Focus**	**Organization**	**Development of Evidence**	**Language and Vocabulary**	**Conventions**
4	Opinion is clearly conveyed and well supported; response is focused.	Organization is clear and effective, creating a sense of cohesion.	Evidence is thorough and persuasive, and includes facts and details.	Ideas are clearly and effectively conveyed, using precise language and/or domain-specific vocabulary.	Command of conventions is strongly demonstrated.
3	Opinion is clear, adequately supported; response is generally focused.	Organization is clear, though minor flaws may be present and some ideas may be disconnected.	Evidence is adequate and includes facts and details.	Ideas are adequately conveyed, using both precise and more general language; may include domain-specific vocabulary.	Command of conventions is sufficiently demonstrated.
2	Opinion is somewhat supported; response may lack focus or include unnecessary material.	Organization is inconsistent, and flaws are apparent.	Evidence is uneven or incomplete; insufficient use of facts and details.	Ideas are unevenly conveyed, using overly-simplistic language; lack of domain-specific vocabulary.	Command of conventions is uneven.
1	The response may be confusing, unfocused; opinion not sufficiently supported.	Organization is poor or nonexistent.	Evidence is poor or nonexistent.	Ideas are conveyed in a vague, unclear, or confusing manner.	There is very little command of conventions.
0	The response shows no evidence of the ability to construct a coherent opinion essay using information from sources.				

© Common Core State Standards

Writing 1. Write opinion pieces in which they introduce the topic or name the book they are writing about, state an opinion, supply a reason for the opinion, and provide some sense of closure.

Name_____

Write Like a Reporter
Argument: Paragraph

Student Prompt Reread the first paragraph of page 140 of *Simple Machines*. Imagine if there were no machines. Which machine do you think would be the most difficult to live without? Write a short paragraph that tells your opinion and tell why you chose that machine. Be sure to write reasons that support your opinion. Use evidence from the text and photographs.

_____

_____

_____

_____

_____

_____

_____

_____

_____

_____

_____

_____

_____

_____

Write Like a Reporter
Argumentative Paragraph

> **Student Prompt, p. 198** Reread the first paragraph of page 140 of *Simple Machines*. Imagine if there were no machines. Which machine do you think would be the most difficult to live without? Write a short paragraph that tells your opinion and tell why you chose that machine. Be sure to write reasons that support your opinion. Use evidence from the text and photographs.

Writing to Sources Review *Simple Machines*. Discuss the photographs with children. Prompt them in identifying how different machines help get a job done more easily. Ask children to think about each machine and decide which they think would be most difficult to live without. Point out that they need reasons that support their opinion, and they will write these reasons. Have children look for details in the text and photographs they can use as supporting evidence.

Children's paragraphs should:

- introduce the topic
- state an opinion
- supply a reason to support the opinion
- provide some sense of closure
- demonstrate strong command of the conventions of standard written English

---

© Common Core State Standards

Writing 1. Write opinion pieces in which they introduce the topic or name the book they are writing about, state an opinion, supply a reason for the opinion, and provide some sense of closure.

Name_____

Connect the Texts
Argument: Paragraph

Student Prompt *Simple Machines* and "Roy's Wheelchair" are about many kinds of machines. Review the text and photographs in both selections. Which machine do you think is the most interesting? Write a short paragraph that tells your opinion. Use evidence from both texts to support your choice.

_____

_____

_____

_____

_____

_____

_____

_____

_____

_____

_____

_____

_____

_____

Connect the Texts
Argumentative Paragraph

Student Prompt, p. 200 *Simple Machines* and "Roy's Wheelchair" are about many kinds of machines. Review the text and photographs in both selections. Which machine do you think is the most interesting? Write a short paragraph that tells your opinion. Use evidence from both texts to support your choice.

Writing to Sources Have children examine the text and photographs of *Simple Machines* and "Roy's Wheelchair." After they review the two texts, discuss with children which machine they find the most interesting and why. Ask them if what the machine is able to do influenced their opinion. Then have children write their opinion. Remind them of the importance of supporting the opinion with concrete details from the selections.

	4-point Argument Writing Rubric				
Score	**Statement of Purpose/Focus**	**Organization**	**Development of Evidence**	**Language and Vocabulary**	**Conventions**
4	Opinion is clearly conveyed and well supported; response is focused.	Organization is clear and effective, creating a sense of cohesion.	Evidence is thorough and persuasive, and includes facts and details.	Ideas are clearly and effectively conveyed, using precise language and/or domain-specific vocabulary.	Command of conventions is strongly demonstrated.
3	Opinion is clear, adequately supported; response is generally focused.	Organization is clear, though minor flaws may be present and some ideas may be disconnected.	Evidence is adequate and includes facts and details.	Ideas are adequately conveyed, using both precise and more general language; may include domain-specific vocabulary.	Command of conventions is sufficiently demonstrated.
2	Opinion is somewhat supported; response may lack focus or include unnecessary material.	Organization is inconsistent, and flaws are apparent.	Evidence is uneven or incomplete; insufficient use of facts and details.	Ideas are unevenly conveyed, using overly-simplistic language; lack of domain-specific vocabulary.	Command of conventions is uneven.
1	The response may be confusing, unfocused; opinion not sufficiently supported.	Organization is poor or nonexistent.	Evidence is poor or nonexistent.	Ideas are conveyed in a vague, unclear, or confusing manner.	There is very little command of conventions.
0	The response shows no evidence of the ability to construct a coherent opinion essay using information from sources.				

Common Core State Standards

Writing 1. Write opinion pieces in which they introduce the topic or name the book they are writing about, state an opinion, supply a reason for the opinion, and provide some sense of closure.

Name_____

Write Like a Reporter

Argument: Paragraph

Student Prompt Reread page 185 of *Alexander Graham Bell: A Great Inventor*. Do you think Bell made the right choice when he decided to focus on inventing? Write a short paragraph that tells your opinion. Support your opinion with reasons. Use evidence from the text.

_____

_____

_____

_____

_____

_____

_____

_____

_____

_____

_____

_____

_____

_____

Write Like a Reporter
Argumentative Paragraph

Student Prompt, p. 202 Reread page 185 of *Alexander Graham Bell: A Great Inventor*. Do you think Bell made the right choice when he decided to focus on inventing? Write a short paragraph that tells your opinion. Support your opinion with reasons. Use evidence from the text.

Writing to Sources Review *Alexander Graham Bell: A Great Inventor*. Discuss with children how Bell helped others as a teacher and how he helped others as an inventor. The text on pages 184 and 192 are helpful in guiding this discussion. Then have children share their opinions of Bell's choice to focus on inventing. Direct them to write their opinion and provide reasons that support their opinion. Have children look for details in the story they can use as their reasons.

Children's paragraphs should:

- introduce the topic
- state an opinion
- supply a reason for the opinion that is supported by text evidence
- provide some sense of closure
- demonstrate strong command of the conventions of standard written English

---

Ⓒ **Common Core State Standards**

Writing 1. Write opinion pieces in which they introduce the topic or name the book they are writing about, state an opinion, supply a reason for the opinion, and provide some sense of closure.

Connect the Texts

Argument: Paragraph

Student Prompt *Alexander Graham Bell: A Great Inventor* and "Inventions" are about inventions. Review the text and illustrations or photographs in each selection. Do you think every invention in the texts is an important invention? Write a short paragraph that tells your opinion. Support your opinion by writing details from both texts.

_____

- -

_____

- -

_____

- -

_____

- -

_____

- -

_____

- -

_____

- -

_____

- -

_____

Connect the Texts
Argumentative Paragraph

Student Prompt, p. 204 *Alexander Graham Bell: A Great Inventor* and "Inventions" are about inventions. Review the text and illustrations or photographs in each selection. Do you think every invention in the texts is an important invention? Write a short paragraph that tells your opinion. Support your opinion by writing details from both texts.

Writing to Sources Discuss the inventions in each selection with children and whether they think they are important. If children have difficulty identifying why eyeglasses are an important invention, ask them to consider how they help people. Then have children write their opinion, supporting it with evidence from each text. After children have completed their opinion pieces, take a survey to discover how many thought each invention was important, and how many did not.

		4-point Argument Writing Rubric			
Score	**Statement of Purpose/Focus**	**Organization**	**Development of Evidence**	**Language and Vocabulary**	**Conventions**
4	Opinion is clearly conveyed and well supported; response is focused.	Organization is clear and effective, creating a sense of cohesion.	Evidence is thorough and persuasive, and includes facts and details.	Ideas are clearly and effectively conveyed, using precise language and/or domain-specific vocabulary.	Command of conventions is strongly demonstrated.
3	Opinion is clear, adequately supported; response is generally focused.	Organization is clear, though minor flaws may be present and some ideas may be disconnected.	Evidence is adequate and includes facts and details.	Ideas are adequately conveyed, using both precise and more general language; may include domain-specific vocabulary.	Command of conventions is sufficiently demonstrated.
2	Opinion is somewhat supported; response may lack focus or include unnecessary material.	Organization is inconsistent, and flaws are apparent.	Evidence is uneven or incomplete; insufficient use of facts and details.	Ideas are unevenly conveyed, using overly-simplistic language; lack of domain-specific vocabulary.	Command of conventions is uneven.
1	The response may be confusing, unfocused; opinion not sufficiently supported.	Organization is poor or nonexistent.	Evidence is poor or nonexistent.	Ideas are conveyed in a vague, unclear, or confusing manner.	There is very little command of conventions.
0	The response shows no evidence of the ability to construct a coherent opinion essay using information from sources.				

© Common Core State Standards

Writing 1. Write opinion pieces in which they introduce the topic or name the book they are writing about, state an opinion, supply a reason for the opinion, and provide some sense of closure.

Write Like a Reporter

Argument: Paragraph

Student Prompt Reread page 226 of *The Stone Garden*. Momoko's neighbors work together to help her create the garden. Was that a good idea or should they have let Momoko create the garden herself? Write a short paragraph that tells your opinion. Write reasons that support your opinion. Use evidence from the text.

_____
_____
_____
_____
_____
_____
_____
_____
_____
_____
_____
_____
_____
_____

Write Like a Reporter
Argumentative Paragraph

Student Prompt, p. 206 Reread page 226 of *The Stone Garden*. Momoko's neighbors work together to help her create the garden. Was that a good idea or should they have let Momoko create the garden herself? Write a short paragraph that tells your opinion. Write reasons that support your opinion. Use evidence from the text.

Writing to Sources Have children review pages 220–226 of *The Stone Garden*. Make a list of the neighbors' contributions to the garden on the board. Direct children to examine the illustration on pages 226–227. Ask them to consider if Momoko could have added all of the features depicted in the garden herself. Then have children decide whether it was a good idea for the neighbors to help Momoko. Once children form an opinion, have them write their reasons for that opinion to help readers understand their choice. Ask children to locate details in the story they can use to support their opinion.

Children's paragraphs should:

- introduce the topic
- state a clear opinion about the topic
- supply reasons for the opinion
- provide some sense of closure
- demonstrate strong command of the conventions of standard written English

---

© **Common Core State Standards**

Writing 1. Write opinion pieces in which they introduce the topic or name the book they are writing about, state an opinion, supply a reason for the opinion, and provide some sense of closure.

Connect the Texts

Argument: Paragraph

Student Prompt *The Stone Garden*, "Common Language," and "A Map and a Dream" each tell an idea about people or the world. Describe each idea. Which idea do you like best? Write a short paragraph that tells your opinion. Find details in the text and illustrations that support your opinion. Write these details.

_____

_____

_____

_____

_____

_____

_____

_____

_____

_____

_____

_____

_____

_____

_____

_____

_____

_____

Connect the Texts
Argumentative Paragraph

Student Prompt, p. 208 *The Stone Garden*, "Common Language," and "A Map and a Dream" each tell an idea about people or the world. Describe each idea. Which idea do you like best? Write a short paragraph that tells your opinion. Find details in the text and illustrations that support your opinion. Write these details.

Writing to Sources Discuss the ideas in the selection and poems with children (*The Stone Garden*: a community works together to create something; "Common Language": laughter is a universal language; "A Map and a Dream": using a map to travel in one's imagination). Children may perceive other ideas in the selections. Accept all reasonable contributions to the discussion. Have children select the idea they like best. Then ask them to write their opinion and give facts and details from the selection to support the opinion.

		4-point Argument Writing Rubric			
Score	Statement of Purpose/Focus	Organization	Development of Evidence	Language and Vocabulary	Conventions
4	Opinion is clearly conveyed and well supported; response is focused.	Organization is clear and effective, creating a sense of cohesion.	Evidence is thorough and persuasive, and includes facts and details.	Ideas are clearly and effectively conveyed, using precise language and/or domain-specific vocabulary.	Command of conventions is strongly demonstrated.
3	Opinion is clear, adequately supported; response is generally focused.	Organization is clear, though minor flaws may be present and some ideas may be disconnected.	Evidence is adequate and includes facts and details.	Ideas are adequately conveyed, using both precise and more general language; may include domain-specific vocabulary.	Command of conventions is sufficiently demonstrated.
2	Opinion is somewhat supported; response may lack focus or include unnecessary material.	Organization is inconsistent, and flaws are apparent.	Evidence is uneven or incomplete; insufficient use of facts and details.	Ideas are unevenly conveyed, using overly-simplistic language; lack of domain-specific vocabulary.	Command of conventions is uneven.
1	The response may be confusing, unfocused; opinion not sufficiently supported.	Organization is poor or nonexistent.	Evidence is poor or nonexistent.	Ideas are conveyed in a vague, unclear, or confusing manner.	There is very little command of conventions.
0	The response shows no evidence of the ability to construct a coherent opinion essay using information from sources.				

© **Common Core State Standards**

Writing 1. Write opinion pieces in which they introduce the topic or name the book they are writing about, state an opinion, supply a reason for the opinion, and provide some sense of closure.

Prove It!
Opinion Paragraph

Academic Vocabulary

An opinion paragraph is a type of argument or opinion writing. In opinion writing, the writer tells what he or she thinks about a topic, an issue, or a text.

ELL

Introduce Genre Write *opinion paragraph* on the board. Explain that this names a kind of writing that tries to persuade people to think or act in a certain way. The writing always gives reasons why the reader should agree with the writer. Discuss with children the key features of an opinion paragraph that appear on this page.

My Favorite Invention

Opinion Paragraph

In this unit, children have read examples of argument writing, including opinion pieces, and have had the opportunity to write in this mode. Remind children of texts and writing tasks (such as Write Like a Reporter and Connect the Texts) in which they have encountered and practiced argument writing.

Key Features of an Opinion Paragraph

- begins with an introductory statement that tells what the paragraph is about
- states the writer's opinion on the topic
- supports the opinion with reasons backed by facts and details from the source
- provides a concluding statement that summarizes the writer's main point

Writing Task Overview

Each unit writing task provides children with an opportunity to write to sources. To successfully complete the task, children must analyze, synthesize, and evaluate multiple complex texts and create their own written response.

My Favorite Invention

Part 1: Children will read the selections and review the information about the selections. They can take notes or draw pictures for these sources. They will then respond to several questions about these sources and discuss their written responses with partners or in small groups.

Part 2: Children will work individually to plan, write, and revise their own opinion paragraph.

Scorable Products: evidence-based short response, opinion paragraph

My Favorite Invention: Writing Task – Short Response

Teacher Directions:

1. Introduce the Sources Refer children to the following texts in the Student Edition:

     1. *Simple Machines,* pp. 138–155

     2. *Alexander Graham Bell: A Great Inventor,* pp. 174–193

Explain to children that they will need to draw evidence and support from the texts above in order to answer evidence-based short response questions and to write an opinion paragraph. Children may draw or take notes as they closely reread the texts. Children should be given paper or a relevant graphic organizer from the TR DVD for note-taking.

2. Provide Directions (pp. 214–215) Answer any task-related questions children may have.

3. Facilitate Collaboration After children have completed their written responses to the evidence-based short response questions, assign partners or small groups and have them discuss their responses. If children struggle to work together productively, provide them with tips and strategies for expressing their ideas and building on others'.

© **Common Core State Standards**

Writing 1. Write opinion pieces in which they introduce the topic or name the book they are writing about, state an opinion, supply a reason for the opinion, and provide some sense of closure.

Scoring Information

Use the following 2-point scoring rubrics to evaluate children's answers to the evidence-based short response questions.

1. Tell about the different machines and inventions in the selections. What do they do?

	Analysis Rubric
2	The response: • demonstrates the ability to analyze facts and details about machines and inventions across the texts • includes specific details that make reference to the texts
1	The response: • demonstrates a limited ability to analyze facts and details about machines and inventions across the texts • includes some details that make reference to the texts
0	A response receives no credit if it demonstrates no ability to analyze facts and details across the texts or includes no relevant details from the texts.

2. How can machines and inventions make our lives better? Give examples from the texts that show how machines and inventions can help people.

Synthesis Rubric	
2	The response: • demonstrates the ability to synthesize information from the sources in order to describe how machines and inventions improve people's lives • includes specific details that make reference to the texts
1	The response: • demonstrates a limited ability to synthesize information from the sources in order to describe how machines and inventions improve people's lives • includes some details that make reference to the texts
0	A response receives no credit if it demonstrates no ability to synthesize information from the sources or includes no relevant details from the texts.

Ⓒ **Common Core State Standards**

Writing 1. Write opinion pieces in which they introduce the topic or name the book they are writing about, state an opinion, supply a reason for the opinion, and provide some sense of closure.

My Favorite Invention
Writing Task – Short Response

I. Tell about the different machines and inventions in the selections. What do they do?

_____

_____

_____

_____

_____

_____

_____

_____

_____

_____

_____

_____

_____

Name _____

2. How can machines and inventions make our lives better? Give examples from the texts that show how machines and inventions can help people.

Let's Discuss

After you have written your responses to the questions, discuss your ideas. Your teacher will assign you a partner or a small group.

My Favorite Invention: Writing Task – Opinion Paragraph

Teacher Directions:

1. Provide Directions (p. 218) Explain to children that they will now review their notes and sources and plan, draft, and revise their opinion paragraphs. Although they may use their notes and sources, they must work alone. Children will be allowed to look back at the answers they wrote to the short response questions, but they are not allowed to make changes to those answers. Have children read the directions for the opinion paragraph and answer any task-related questions they may have. Children should be given paper on which to write their paragraphs.

2. Scoring Information Use the scoring rubric on the next page to evaluate children's opinion paragraphs.

3. Opinion Paragraph Prompt Write a paragraph telling which of the machines or inventions you like best. State your opinion and support it with reasons. Use examples from the two selections to defend your choice.

	Argument Writing Rubric				
Score	Statement of Purpose/Focus	Organization	Development of Evidence	Language and Vocabulary	Conventions
4	Paragraph clearly states and supports opinion.	Organization includes a clear opinion and strong reasons.	Evidence includes sufficient facts and details.	Linking words are effectively used to connect ideas.	Use of conventions is clearly shown.
3	Paragraph adequately states and supports opinion.	Organization includes an opinion and reasons.	Evidence includes some facts and details.	Linking words are used to connect ideas.	Use of conventions is somewhat shown.
2	Paragraph somewhat supports opinion.	Organization lacks an opinion; unclear reasons.	Evidence does not include facts and details.	Few linking words are used.	Use of conventions is uneven.
1	Paragraph is confusing; opinion is not supported.	Organization lacks opinion and reasons.	Evidence is poor or nonexistent.	There is little or no use of linking words.	There is very little correct use of conventions.
0	The response shows no evidence of the ability to construct a coherent paragraph using information from sources.				

© Common Core State Standards

Writing 1. Write opinion pieces in which they introduce the topic or name the book they are writing about, state an opinion, supply a reason for the opinion, and provide some sense of closure.

My Favorite Invention

Writing Task – Opinion Paragraph

Opinion Paragraph Prompt

Write a paragraph telling which of the machines or inventions you like best. State your opinion and support it with reasons. Use examples from the two selections to defend your choice.

_____

_____

_____

_____

_____

_____

_____

_____

_____

_____

_____

_____

_____

_____

_____

_____

_____

_____

_____

_____

My Favorite Invention: Writing Task – Opinion Paragraph

Teacher Directions:

1. Publish Explain to children that publishing their writing is the last step in the writing process. If time permits, have children look at one another's compositions and incorporate any comments their classmates have. Discuss different ways technology can be used to publish writing.

2. Present Children will now have the option to present their opinion paragraphs. Have children read aloud their paragraphs to the class. Use the list below to offer children tips on listening and speaking.

While Listening to a Classmate...
- Listen carefully.
- Think of relevant questions.

While Speaking to Classmates...
- Speak clearly at an appropriate pace.
- Face the audience.

Things to Do Together...
- Build on others' ideas.
- Ask questions to check understanding.

© **Common Core State Standards**

Writing 1. Write opinion pieces in which they introduce the topic or name the book they are writing about, state an opinion, supply a reason for the opinion, and provide some sense of closure.

More Connect the Texts

More Connect the Texts
Persuasive Text

Objectives

- Identify the characteristics of persuasive text.
- Write persuasive text, using facts and supporting details.
- Evaluate your writing.
- Revise and publish your writing.

© Common Core State Standards

Writing 1. Write opinion pieces in which they introduce the topic or name the book they are writing about, state an opinion, supply a reason for the opinion, and provide some sense of closure. **Writing 5.** With guidance and support from adults, focus on a topic, respond to questions and suggestions from peers, and add details to strengthen writing as needed.

STEP 1 Read Like a Writer

Review the key features of persuasive text listed below. Respond to any questions children might have.

Key Features of Persuasive Text

- States the writer's opinion about a topic
- Supports the opinion with facts and reasons
- Uses opinion words such as *important* and *best*
- Often organizes reasons in order of importance
- Provides a concluding statement

Choose an opinion piece or persuasive text that children have already read to model key features. Display the model for children to see, and point out each key feature you have discussed.

STEP 2 Organize Your Ideas

Writing Prompt Look back at "They Can Help" and *Animal Park*. Write a short, persuasive text that tells which animal from the selections is the most interesting to you. Be sure your opinion is clearly written. Support your opinion with facts and reasons from the texts. Use opinion words such as *best* and *important*.

Think Aloud Your ideas will be more convincing if they are well organized. Decide on the opinion you will state in your piece. Then decide what facts and reasons from the texts you will use to support your opinion. You may wish to fill in a chart before you begin writing.

Guided Writing Display a chart with four boxes as an example. Show children how to write their opinion in the first box and then write the reasons that support their opinion in the other three boxes. Explain to them that when they write, they will first state their opinion, then arrange their reasons in a logical order. Finally, they will end with a statement that sums up their opinion.

STEP 3 Draft Your Writing

Have children use their charts to write their persuasive texts. Remind them of the key features of persuasive text.

Think Aloud One of the best ways to support your opinion is to use facts and reasons. You can find facts and reasons by rereading "They Can Help" and *Animal Park*. You can also look at books, articles, and Web sites to find additional facts about your animal.

Getting Started Tell children to begin writing their text using their charts to keep them on track. Remind them to use opinion words such as *best* and *important*. Also emphasize the importance of using correct grammar and complete sentences.

STEP 4 Evaluate Your Writing

Display the checklist below and have children use it to evaluate their persuasive texts. Circulate around the room and confer with individual children.

✓ Did I state my opinion clearly?

✓ Did I use facts and reasons to support my opinion?

✓ Did I use opinion words?

✓ Does my concluding statement sum up my opinion?

✓ Did I use correct grammar, spelling, capitalization, and punctuation?

Help children set goals and make a plan for improving in areas where their writing needs help.

STEP 5 Revise and Publish

Help children follow through with their plans for revision. If time permits, have children trade texts and offer suggestions for how to improve the writing.

Publishing Children can publish their texts by posting them on a class bulletin board or in a hall display case.

More Connect the Texts
Review

Objectives

- Identify the characteristics of a story review.
- Write a review, using words that tell how you feel about the story.
- Evaluate your writing.
- Revise and publish your writing.

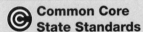 **Common Core State Standards**

Writing 1. Write opinion pieces in which they introduce the topic or name the book they are writing about, state an opinion, supply a reason for the opinion, and provide some sense of closure. **Writing 5.** With guidance and support from adults, focus on a topic, respond to questions and suggestions from peers, and add details to strengthen writing as needed.

STEP 1 Read Like a Writer

Review the key features of a review listed below. Respond to any questions children might have.

Key Features of a Review

- Clearly states the name of the story
- Tells the writer's opinion about the story
- Tells the reasons for the writer's opinion
- Uses feeling words such as *happy* and *sad*
- Provides a concluding statement

Choose a short, simple review from a magazine or newspaper to model key features. Display the model for children to see, and point out each key feature you have discussed.

STEP 2 Organize Your Ideas

Writing Prompt Look back at *Pig in a Wig* and *Get the Egg!* Write a short review of each story. Tell about something Pig does that you like. Tell about something Brad or Kim does that you like. Be sure your reasons are clearly written. Use feeling words such as *happy* and *sad.* Cite evidence from the texts to support your opinion.

Think Aloud Your reviews will be more interesting if they are focused. Decide what each character does that you like. Then make a list. Then you can choose one thing to write about.

Guided Writing Display a list with three or four items as an example. List a character's main actions.

What Kim Does

- Kim tells Brad to catch the egg.
- Kim sets the egg back in the nest.

What Pig Does

- Pig eats too much.
- Pig dances.

Have each child use a list to choose something they like that a character does from each story. Circulate to guide them. Have them tell why they like their choices.

STEP 3 Draft Your Writing

Have children write their reviews. Remind them of the key features of a review.

Think Aloud One of the best ways to write an interesting review is to use feeling words. You can tell what a character did and tell how you felt using feeling words. You can reread *Get the Egg!* or *Pig in a Wig* as reminders.

Getting Started Tell children to begin writing their reviews. Remind them to use feeling words such as *happy* and *sad.* Also emphasize the importance of using correct grammar and complete sentences.

STEP 4 Evaluate Your Writing

Display the checklist below and have children use it to evaluate their reviews. Circulate around the room and confer with individual children.

- ✓ Did I name both stories?
- ✓ Did I tell my opinion clearly?
- ✓ Did I give reasons for my opinion?
- ✓ Did I use feeling words?
- ✓ Does my concluding statement sum up my comments?
- ✓ Did I use correct grammar, spelling, capitalization, and punctuation?

Help children set goals and make a plan for improving in areas where their writing needs help.

STEP 5 Revise and Publish

Help children follow through with their plans for revision. If time permits, have children trade reviews and offer suggestions for how to improve the writing.

Publishing Children can publish their reviews by reading them to the class. Children could also post their reviews on a class bulletin board or in a hall display case.

Persuasive Text

Objectives

- Identify the characteristics of persuasive text.
- Write persuasive text, using facts and supporting details.
- Evaluate your writing.
- Revise and publish your writing.

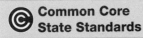
Common Core State Standards

Writing 1. Write opinion pieces in which they introduce the topic or name the book they are writing about, state an opinion, supply a reason for the opinion, and provide some sense of closure. **Writing 5.** With guidance and support from adults, focus on a topic, respond to questions and suggestions from peers, and add details to strengthen writing as needed. **Writing 6.** With guidance and support from adults, use a variety of digital tools to produce and publish writing, including in collaboration with peers.

STEP 1 Read Like a Writer

Review the key features of persuasive text listed below. Respond to any questions children might have.

Key Features of Persuasive Text

- States the writer's opinion about a topic
- Supports the opinion with facts and reasons
- Uses persuasive words such as *best* and *must*
- Often organizes reasons in order of importance
- Provides a concluding statement

Choose an opinion piece or persuasive text that children have already read to model key features. Display the model for children to see. Point out each key feature you have discussed.

STEP 2 Organize Your Ideas

Writing Prompt Look back at *Get the Egg!* and "Help the Birds." Which selection best shows how to be kind to birds? Write a short persuasive text that tells your opinion. Support your opinion with facts and reasons from the texts. Include persuasive words such as *must* and *best.*

Think Aloud Your opinions will be more convincing if they are well organized. Decide on the opinion you will write about in your text. Then decide what facts and reasons you will use to support your opinion. You may wish to fill in a chart before you begin writing.

Guided Writing Display a chart with four boxes as an example. Show children how to write their opinion in the first box, and then write the facts and reasons that support their opinion in the other three boxes. Explain to them that when they write, they will first state their opinion, then arrange their facts and reasons in a logical order, and finally end with a statement that sums up their opinion.

STEP 3 Draft Your Writing

Have children use their charts to write persuasive text. Remind them of the key features of persuasive text.

Think Aloud One of the best ways to persuade readers is to use facts and reasons that support your opinion. You can find facts and reasons by looking back at the selections. You also want to be sure you use persuasive words, such as *best* and *must.*

Getting Started Tell children to begin writing their persuasive texts using their charts to help them. Offer suggestions on how to organize their texts with facts and supporting reasons. Remind them to use persuasive words such as *best* and *must.* Emphasize the importance of using correct grammar and complete sentences. Remind them to end their texts with a concluding statement.

STEP 4 Evaluate Your Writing

Display the checklist below and have children use it to evaluate their texts. Circulate around the room and confer with individual children.

✓ Did I state my opinion clearly?

✓ Do my facts and reasons support my opinion?

✓ Did I use persuasive words?

✓ Does my concluding statement make sense?

✓ Did I use correct grammar, spelling, capitalization, and punctuation?

Help children set goals and make a plan for improving in areas where their writing needs help.

STEP 5 Revise and Publish

Help children follow through with their plans for revision. If time permits, have children trade texts and offer suggestions for how to improve the writing.

Publishing Children can publish their persuasive texts by reading them to the class. Children could also use a computer to make a final draft of their texts. The printed copies can then be displayed on a class bulletin board.

More Connect the Texts
Persuasive Text

Objectives

- Identify the characteristics of persuasive text.
- Write persuasive text, using facts and supporting reasons.
- Evaluate your writing.
- Revise and publish your writing.

Common Core State Standards

Writing 1. Write opinion pieces in which they introduce the topic or name the book they are writing about, state an opinion, supply a reason for the opinion, and provide some sense of closure. **Writing 5.** With guidance and support from adults, focus on a topic, respond to questions and suggestions from peers, and add details to strengthen writing as needed.

STEP 1 Read Like a Writer

Review the key features of persuasive text listed below. Respond to any questions children might have.

Key Features of Persuasive Text

- States the writer's opinion about a topic
- Supports the opinion with facts and reasons
- Uses persuasive words such as *best* and *must*
- Often organizes reasons in order of importance
- Provides a concluding statement

Choose an opinion piece or persuasive text that children have already read to model key features. Display the model for children to see. Point out each key feature you have discussed.

STEP 2 Organize Your Ideas

Writing Prompt Look back at *Who Works Here?* and "Helping Hands at 4-H." Which person or group is most helpful to people? Write a short persuasive text that tells your opinion. Support your opinion with facts and reasons from the text. Include persuasive words such as *must* and *best.*

Think Aloud Your opinions will be more convincing if they are well organized. Decide on the opinion you will write about in your text. Then decide which facts and reasons you will use to support your opinion. You may wish to fill in a chart before you begin writing.

Guided Writing Display a chart with four boxes as an example. Show children how to write their opinion in the first box, and then write the facts and reasons that support their opinion in the other three boxes. Explain to them that when they write, they will first state their opinion, then arrange their facts and reasons in a logical order, and finally end with a statement that sums up their opinion.

STEP 3 Draft Your Writing

Have children use their charts to write persuasive text. Remind them of the key features of persuasive text.

Think Aloud One of the best ways to persuade readers is to use facts and reasons to support your opinion. You can find facts and reasons by looking back at the selections. You also want to be sure you use persuasive words, such as *best* and *must.*

Getting Started Tell children to begin writing their persuasive texts using their charts to help them. Suggest supporting reasons for children having difficulty completing their ideas. Remind them to use persuasive words and to end their texts with a concluding statement. Emphasize the importance of using correct grammar and complete sentences.

STEP 4 Evaluate Your Writing

Display the checklist below and have children use it to evaluate their persuasive texts. Circulate around the room and confer with individual children.

- ✓ Did I state my opinion clearly?
- ✓ Do my facts and reasons support my opinion?
- ✓ Did I use persuasive words?
- ✓ Does my concluding statement make sense?
- ✓ Did I use correct grammar, spelling, capitalization, and punctuation?

Help children set goals and make a plan for improving in areas where their writing needs help.

STEP 5 Revise and Publish

Help children follow through with their plans for revision. If time permits, have children trade texts and offer suggestions for how to improve the writing.

Publishing Children can publish their persuasive texts by displaying them on a class bulletin board or in a hallway display case.

More Connect the Texts
Persuasive Text

Objectives

- Identify the characteristics of persuasive text.
- Write persuasive text, using facts and supporting reasons.
- Evaluate your writing.
- Revise and publish your writing.

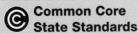
Common Core State Standards

Writing 1. Write opinion pieces in which they introduce the topic or name the book they are writing about, state an opinion, supply a reason for the opinion, and provide some sense of closure. **Writing 5.** With guidance and support from adults, focus on a topic, respond to questions and suggestions from peers, and add details to strengthen writing as needed. **Writing 6.** With guidance and support from adults, use a variety of digital tools to produce and publish writing, including in collaboration with peers.

STEP 1   Read Like a Writer

Review the key features of persuasive text listed below. Respond to any questions children might have.

Key Features of Persuasive Text
- States the writer's opinion about a topic
- Supports the opinion with facts and reasons
- Uses persuasive words such as *best* and *most*
- Often organizes reasons in order of importance
- Provides a concluding statement

Choose an opinion piece or persuasive text that children have already read to model key features. Display the model for children to see. Point out each key feature you have discussed.

STEP 2   Organize Your Ideas

Writing Prompt Look back at *The Big Circle* and *Honey Bees.* Which group is better at defending themselves, dinosaurs or bees? Write a short persuasive text that tells your opinion. Support your opinion with facts and reasons from the text. Include persuasive words such as *best* and *most.*

Think Aloud Your opinions will be more convincing if they are well organized. Decide on the opinion you will write about in your text. Then decide which facts and reasons you will use to support your opinion. You may wish to fill in a chart before you begin writing.

Guided Writing Display a chart with four boxes as an example. Show children how to write their opinion in the first box, and then write the facts and reasons that support their opinion in the other three boxes. Explain to them that when they write, they will first state their opinion, then arrange their facts and reasons in a logical order, and finally end with a statement that sums up their opinion.

STEP 3 Draft Your Writing

Have children use their charts to write persuasive text. Remind them of the key features of persuasive text.

Think Aloud One of the best ways to persuade readers is to use facts and reasons to support your opinion. You can find facts and reasons by looking back at the selections. You also want to be sure you use persuasive words, such as *best* and *most.*

Getting Started Tell children to begin writing their persuasive texts using their charts to help them. Offer suggestions on how to organize their texts with facts and supporting reasons. Remind them to use persuasive words and to end their texts with a concluding statement. Emphasize the importance of using correct grammar and complete sentences.

STEP 4 Evaluate Your Writing

Display the checklist below and have children use it to evaluate their persuasive texts. Circulate around the room and confer with individual children.

- ✓ Did I state my opinion clearly?
- ✓ Do my facts and reasons support my opinion?
- ✓ Did I use persuasive words?
- ✓ Does my concluding statement make sense?
- ✓ Did I use correct grammar, spelling, capitalization, and punctuation?

Help children set goals and make a plan for improving in areas where their writing needs help.

STEP 5 Revise and Publish

Help children follow through with their plans for revision. If time permits, have children trade texts and offer suggestions for how to improve the writing.

Publishing Children can publish their persuasive texts by reading them to the class or to small groups. They can also use a computer to print a final copy of their texts and display them on a class bulletin board.

Advertisement

Objectives

- Identify the characteristics of an advertisement.
- Write an advertisement, using opinions and reasons.
- Evaluate your writing.
- Revise and publish your writing.

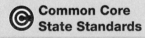

Common Core State Standards

Writing 1. Write opinion pieces in which they introduce the topic or name the book they are writing about, state an opinion, supply a reason for the opinion, and provide some sense of closure. **Writing 5.** With guidance and support from adults, focus on a topic, respond to questions and suggestions from peers, and add details to strengthen writing as needed.

STEP 1 Read Like a Writer

Review the key features of an advertisement listed below. Respond to any questions children might have.

Key Features of an Advertisement

- Promotes a product or service, using opinions and reasons
- Describes the product or service
- Uses persuasive words such as *greatest* and *need*
- Often provides a concluding statement

Choose an advertisement from a magazine or newspaper to model key features. Display the model for children to see. Point out each key feature you have discussed.

STEP 2 Organize Your Ideas

Writing Prompt Look back at *Life in the Forest* and "A Mangrove Forest." What facts did you learn that would make someone want to visit a forest? Write an advertisement to get people to buy tickets for a trip to a forest. Use your opinion and evidence from both selections to get people interested in forests. Include persuasive words such as *greatest* and *need*.

Think Aloud Your advertisement will be more successful if it is well organized. Decide what reasons you will use to support your opinion. You may wish to fill in an idea web before you begin writing.

Guided Writing Display an idea web, with four circles around a center circle, as an example. Show children how to write *buy tickets to visit a forest* in the center circle, and then write the reasons that support their opinion in the other four circles. Explain to them that when they write, they will first state their opinion, then arrange their reasons in a logical order, and finally end with a statement that encourages people to buy tickets.

STEP 3 Draft Your Writing

Have children use their charts to write the advertisement. Remind them of the key features of an advertisement.

Think Aloud Remember that you need to use reasons to support your opinion. People will be more likely to buy tickets if you write good reasons. You can find reasons by looking back at the selections. You also want to be sure you use persuasive words, such as *greatest* and *need.*

Getting Started Tell children to begin writing their advertisements using their webs to help them. Suggest reasons for children having difficulty composing their advertisements. Remind them to use persuasive words and to end their advertisements with a concluding statement, such as *Buy tickets today!* Emphasize the importance of using correct grammar and complete sentences.

STEP 4 Evaluate Your Writing

Display the checklist below and have children use it to evaluate their advertisements. Circulate around the room and confer with individual children.

- ✓ Did I describe my product or service?
- ✓ Do my reasons support my opinion?
- ✓ Did I use persuasive words?
- ✓ Does my concluding statement make sense?
- ✓ Did I use correct grammar, spelling, capitalization, and punctuation?

Help children set goals and make a plan for improving in areas where their writing needs help.

STEP 5 Revise and Publish

Help children follow through with their plans for revision. If time permits, have children trade advertisements and offer suggestions for how to improve the writing.

Publishing Children can publish their advertisements by reading them to the class. They could also create a poster to go along with their advertisements and display them in a hallway display case.

Comments About a Story

Objectives

- Identify the characteristics of comments about a story.
- Write comments about a story, using your opinion and supporting reasons.
- Evaluate your writing.
- Revise and publish your writing.

Common Core State Standards

Writing 1. Write opinion pieces in which they introduce the topic or name the book they are writing about, state an opinion, supply a reason for the opinion, and provide some sense of closure. **Writing 5.** With guidance and support from adults, focus on a topic, respond to questions and suggestions from peers, and add details to strengthen writing as needed.

STEP 1 Read Like a Writer

Review the key features of comments about a story listed below. Respond to any questions children might have.

Key Features of Comments About a Story

- States the writer's opinion about a story
- Supports the opinion with reasons
- Often organizes reasons in order of importance
- Provides a concluding statement

Choose an example of a book review in a children's literary magazine to model key features. Display the model for children to see. Point out each key feature you have discussed.

STEP 2 Organize Your Ideas

Writing Prompt Which part of *Frog and Toad Together* did you like best? Which part of *A Place to Play* did you like best? Write short comments about both stories that tell your opinions. Support your opinions with evidence from the text.

Think Aloud Your opinions will be more convincing if they are well organized. Decide on the parts you like best about each story. Then decide what reasons you will use to support your opinions. You may wish to fill in a chart before you begin writing.

Guided Writing Display a chart of two rows and two columns. Write *I Like. . .* at the top of the first column. Write *Because. . .* at the top of the second column. Write *Frog and Toad Together* at the start of the first row. Write *A Place to Play* at the start of the second row. Show children how to write their opinions in the first column and then write their reasons in the second.

STEP 3 Draft Your Writing

Have children use their charts to write their comments. Remind them of the key features of comments about a story.

Think Aloud One of the best ways to write comments about a story is to use reasons to support your opinion. You have to tell readers why you like a part of a story. Is it funny? Is it exciting? Looking back at the selections can help you think of parts of a story. Looking back can also remind you how you felt when you read that part.

Getting Started Tell children to begin writing their comments using their charts to guide them. Suggest reasons for children having difficulty defending their opinions. Remind them to use a concluding statement with each comment. Emphasize the importance of using correct grammar and complete sentences.

STEP 4 Evaluate Your Writing

Display the checklist below and have children use it to evaluate their comments. Circulate around the room and confer with individual children.

✓ Did I state my opinions clearly?

✓ Do my reasons support my opinion?

✓ Does my concluding statement make sense?

✓ Did I use correct grammar, spelling, capitalization, and punctuation?

Help children set goals and make a plan for improving in areas where their writing needs help.

STEP 5 Revise and Publish

Help children follow through with their plans for revision. If time permits, have children trade their comments and offer suggestions for how to improve the writing.

Publishing Children can publish their comments by displaying them on a class bulletin board. Children could also draw a picture of their favorite story part and display it along with their comments.

Persuasive Text

Objectives

- Identify the characteristics of persuasive text.
- Write persuasive text, using facts and supporting reasons.
- Evaluate your writing.
- Revise and publish your writing.

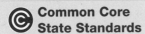
Common Core State Standards

Writing 1. Write opinion pieces in which they introduce the topic or name the book they are writing about, state an opinion, supply a reason for the opinion, and provide some sense of closure. **Writing 5.** With guidance and support from adults, focus on a topic, respond to questions and suggestions from peers, and add details to strengthen writing as needed.

STEP 1 Read Like a Writer

Review the key features of persuasive text listed below. Respond to any questions children might have.

Key Features of Persuasive Text

- States the writer's opinion about a topic
- Supports the opinion with facts and reasons
- Uses persuasive words such as *best* and *most*
- Often organizes reasons in order of importance
- Provides a concluding statement

Choose an opinion piece or persuasive text that children have already read to model key features. Display the model for children to see. Point out each key feature you have discussed.

STEP 2 Organize Your Ideas

Writing Prompt Look back at *The Class Pet* and *I'm a Caterpillar.* Which animal is the most interesting? Write a short, persuasive text that tells your opinion. Support your opinion with evidence from the text. Include persuasive words such as *best* and *most*.

Think Aloud Your opinions will be more convincing if they are well organized. Decide on the opinion you will write about in your text. Then decide what facts and reasons you will use to support your opinion. You may wish to fill in a chart before you begin writing.

Guided Writing Display a chart with four boxes as an example. Show children how to write their opinion in the first box and then write the facts and reasons that support their opinion in the other three boxes. Explain to them that when they write, they will first state their opinion, then arrange their facts and reasons in a logical order, and finally end with a statement that sums up their opinion.

STEP 3 Draft Your Writing

Have children use their charts to write their persuasive text. Remind them of the key features of persuasive text.

Think Aloud One of the best ways to persuade readers is to use facts and reasons to support your opinion. You can find facts and reasons by looking back at the texts. You also want to be sure you use persuasive words, such as *best* and *most*.

Getting Started Tell children to begin writing their persuasive texts using their charts to help them. Suggest supporting reasons for children having difficulty completing their ideas. Remind them to use persuasive words and to end their texts with a concluding statement. Emphasize the importance of using correct grammar and complete sentences.

STEP 4 Evaluate Your Writing

Display the checklist below and have children use it to evaluate their persuasive texts. Circulate around the room and confer with individual children.

- ✓ Did I state my opinion clearly?
- ✓ Do my facts and reasons support my opinion?
- ✓ Did I use persuasive words?
- ✓ Does my concluding statement make sense?
- ✓ Did I use correct grammar, spelling, capitalization, and punctuation?

Help children set goals and make a plan for improving in areas where their writing needs help.

STEP 5 Revise and Publish

Help children follow through with their plans for revision. If time permits, have children trade texts and offer suggestions for how to improve the writing.

Publishing Children can publish their texts by reading them to the class. They can also draw a picture of their animal to show to the class as they read.

More Connect the Texts
Persuasive Text

Objectives

- Identify the characteristics of persuasive text.
- Write persuasive text, using facts and supporting details.
- Evaluate your writing.
- Revise and publish your writing.

Common Core State Standards

Writing 1. Write opinion pieces in which they introduce the topic or name the book they are writing about, state an opinion, supply a reason for the opinion, and provide some sense of closure. **Writing 5.** With guidance and support from adults, focus on a topic, respond to questions and suggestions from peers, and add details to strengthen writing as needed.

STEP 1 Read Like a Writer

Review the key features of persuasive text listed below. Respond to any questions children might have.

Key Features of Persuasive Text

- States the writer's opinion about a topic
- Supports the opinion with facts and reasons
- Uses opinion words such as *most* and *best*
- Often organizes reasons in order of importance
- Provides a concluding statement

Choose an opinion piece or persuasive text that children have already read to model key features. Display the model for children to see, and point out each key feature you have discussed.

STEP 2 Organize Your Ideas

Writing Prompt Look back at *A Trip to Washington, D.C.* and *A Southern Ranch*. Which place would be best for a class field trip? Write a short, persuasive text that persuades the class to visit either a southern ranch or Washington, D.C. Be sure your opinion is clearly written. Support your opinion with facts and reasons from both texts. Use opinion words such as *best* and *most.*

Think Aloud Your ideas will be more convincing if they are well organized. Decide on the opinion you will state in your piece. Then decide what facts and reasons from the texts you will use to support your opinion. You may wish to fill in a chart before you begin writing.

Guided Writing Display a chart with four boxes as an example. Show children how to write their opinion in the first box, and then write the reasons that support their opinion in the other three boxes. Explain to them that when they write, they will first state their opinion, and then arrange their reasons in a logical order. Finally, they will end with a statement that sums up their opinion.

STEP 3 Draft Your Writing

Have children use their charts to write their persuasive texts. Remind them of the key features of persuasive text.

Think Aloud One of the best ways to support your opinion is to use facts and reasons. You can find facts and reasons by rereading the texts. You can also look at books, articles, and Web sites to find additional facts about southern ranches or Washington, D.C.

Getting Started Tell children to begin writing their text using their charts to keep them on track. Remind them to use opinion words such as *best* and *most*. Also emphasize the importance of using correct grammar and complete sentences.

STEP 4 Evaluate Your Writing

Display the checklist below and have children use it to evaluate their persuasive texts. Circulate around the room and confer with individual children.

✓ Did I state my opinion clearly?

✓ Did I use facts and reasons to support my opinion?

✓ Did I use opinion words?

✓ Does my concluding statement sum up my opinion?

✓ Did I use correct grammar, spelling, capitalization, and punctuation?

Help children set goals and make a plan for improving in areas where their writing needs help.

STEP 5 Revise and Publish

Help children follow through with their plans for revision. If time permits, have children trade texts and offer suggestions for how to improve the writing.

Publishing Children can publish their texts by posting them on a class bulletin board or in a hall display case.

Comments About a Story

Objectives

- Identify the characteristics of comments about a story.
- Write comments about a story, using your opinion and supporting reasons.
- Evaluate your writing.
- Revise and publish your writing.

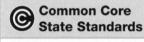

Common Core State Standards

Writing 1. Write opinion pieces in which they introduce the topic or name the book they are writing about, state an opinion, supply a reason for the opinion, and provide some sense of closure. **Writing 5.** With guidance and support from adults, focus on a topic, respond to questions and suggestions from peers, and add details to strengthen writing as needed.

STEP 1 Read Like a Writer

Review the key features of comments about a story listed below. Respond to any questions children might have.

Key Features of Comments About a Story
- States the writer's opinion about a story
- Supports the opinion with reasons
- Often organizes reasons in order of importance
- Provides a concluding statement

Choose an example of a book review in a children's literary magazine to model key features. Display the model for children to see. Point out each key feature you have discussed.

STEP 2 Organize Your Ideas

Writing Prompt Which part of *Mama's Birthday Present* did you like best? Which part of *Cinderella* did you like best? Write short comments about both stories that tell your opinions. Support your opinions with reasons from the text.

Think Aloud Your opinions will be more convincing if they are well organized. Decide on the parts you like best about each story. Then decide what reasons you will use to support your opinions. You may wish to fill in a chart before you begin writing.

Guided Writing Display a chart of two rows and two columns. Write *I Like. . .* at the top of the first column. Write *Because. . .* at the top of the second column. Write *Mama's Birthday Present* at the start of the first row. Write *Cinderella* at the start of the second row. Show children how to write their opinions in the first column and then write their reasons in the second.

STEP 3 Draft Your Writing

Have children use their charts to write their comments. Remind them of the key features of comments about a story.

Think Aloud One of the best ways to write comments about a story is to use reasons to support your opinion. You have to tell readers why you like a part of a story. Is it funny? Is it exciting? Looking back at the selections can help you think of parts of a story. Looking back can also remind you how you felt when you read that part.

Getting Started Tell children to begin writing their comments using their charts to guide them. Suggest reasons for children having difficulty defending their opinions. Remind them to use a concluding statement with each comment. Emphasize the importance of using correct grammar and complete sentences.

STEP 4 Evaluate Your Writing

Display the checklist below and have children use it to evaluate their comments. Circulate around the room and confer with individual children.

- ✓ Did I state my opinions clearly?
- ✓ Do my reasons support my opinion?
- ✓ Does my concluding statement make sense?
- ✓ Did I use correct grammar, spelling, capitalization, and punctuation?

Help children set goals and make a plan for improving in areas where their writing needs help.

STEP 5 Revise and Publish

Help children follow through with their plans for revision. If time permits, have children trade their comments and offer suggestions for how to improve the writing.

Publishing Children can publish their comments by displaying them in a hallway display case. Children could also draw a picture of their favorite story part and display it along with their comments.

Persuasive Text

Objectives

- Identify the characteristics of persuasive text.
- Write persuasive text, using facts and supporting details.
- Evaluate your writing.
- Revise and publish your writing.

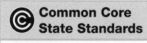
Common Core State Standards

Writing 1. Write opinion pieces in which they introduce the topic or name the book they are writing about, state an opinion, supply a reason for the opinion, and provide some sense of closure. **Writing 5.** With guidance and support from adults, focus on a topic, respond to questions and suggestions from peers, and add details to strengthen writing as needed.

STEP 1 Read Like a Writer

Review the key features of persuasive text listed below. Respond to any questions children might have.

Key Features of Persuasive Text
- States the writer's opinion about a topic
- Supports the opinion with facts and reasons
- Uses opinion words such as *most* and *best*
- Often organizes reasons in order of importance
- Provides a concluding statement

Choose an opinion piece or persuasive text that children have already read to model key features. Display the model for children to see, and point out each key feature you have discussed.

STEP 2 Organize Your Ideas

Writing Prompt Look back at *Mama's Birthday Present* and "My 4th of July." Both texts tell about celebrations. Write a short, persuasive text that tells which celebration is more fun. Be sure your opinion is clearly written. Support your opinion with facts and reasons from both texts. Use opinion words such as *best* and *most*.

Think Aloud Your ideas will be more convincing if they are well organized. Decide on the opinion you will state in your piece. Then decide what facts and reasons from the texts you will use to support your opinion. You may wish to fill in a chart before you begin writing.

Guided Writing Display a chart with four boxes as an example. Show children how to write their opinion in the first box and then write the reasons that support their opinion in the other three boxes. Explain to them that when they write, they will first state their opinion, and then arrange their reasons in a logical order. Finally, they will end with a statement that sums up their opinion.

STEP 3 Draft Your Writing

Have children use their charts to write their persuasive texts. Remind them of the key features of persuasive text.

Think Aloud One of the best ways to support your opinion is to use facts and reasons. You can find facts and reasons by rereading the texts. What did you find out about birthday parties and the 4th of July from reading the texts? What makes them fun?

Getting Started Tell children to begin writing their text using their charts to keep them on track. Remind them to use opinion words such as *best* and *most*. Also emphasize the importance of using correct grammar and complete sentences.

STEP 4 Evaluate Your Writing

Display the checklist below and have children use it to evaluate their persuasive texts. Circulate around the room and confer with individual children.

✓ Did I state my opinion clearly?

✓ Did I use facts and reasons to support my opinion?

✓ Did I use opinion words?

✓ Does my concluding statement sum up my opinion?

✓ Did I use correct grammar, spelling, capitalization, and punctuation?

Help children set goals and make a plan for improving in areas where their writing needs help.

STEP 5 Revise and Publish

Help children follow through with their plans for revision. If time permits, have children trade texts and offer suggestions for how to improve the writing.

Publishing Children can publish their texts by creating a poster with construction paper and crayons. They can attach a final copy of their text to the poster, and display the posters in the classroom.

More Connect the Texts
Advertisement

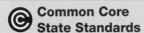
STEP 1 Read Like a Writer

Review the key features of an advertisement listed below. Respond to any questions children might have.

Key Features of an Advertisement
- Promotes a product or service, using opinions and reasons
- Describes the product or service
- Uses persuasive words such as *best* and *need*
- Often provides a concluding statement

Choose an advertisement from a magazine or newspaper to model key features. Display the model for children to see. Point out each key feature you have discussed.

STEP 2 Organize Your Ideas

Writing Prompt Look back at *Simple Machines* and *Alexander Graham Bell: A Great Inventor.* Write an advertisement to get people to buy a machine or invention from one of the selections. Use your opinion and reasons from the text to get people interested in your choice. Include persuasive words such as *best* and *need.*

Think Aloud Your advertisement will be more successful if it is well organized. Decide what reasons you will use to support your opinion. You may wish to fill in an idea web before you begin writing.

Guided Writing Display an idea web, with four circles around a center circle, as an example. Show children how to write the name of their chosen machine or invention in the center circle and then write the reasons that support their opinion in the other four circles. Explain to them that when they write, they will first state their opinion, then arrange their reasons in a logical order, and finally end with a statement that encourages people to buy the machine or invention they chose.

STEP 3 Draft Your Writing

Have children use their charts to write their advertisements. Remind them of the key features of an advertisement.

Think Aloud Remember that you need to use reasons to support your opinion. People will be more likely to buy the machine or invention if you write good reasons. You can find reasons by looking back at the selections. You also want to be sure you use persuasive words, such as *best* and *need.*

Getting Started Tell children to begin writing their advertisements using their webs to help them. Suggest reasons for children having difficulty composing their advertisements. Remind them to use persuasive words and to end their advertisements with a concluding statement, such as *Don't be left out! Buy one today!* Emphasize the importance of using correct grammar and complete sentences.

STEP 4 Evaluate Your Writing

Display the checklist below and have children use it to evaluate their advertisements. Circulate around the room and confer with individual children.

✓ Did I describe my machine or invention?

✓ Do my reasons support my opinion?

✓ Did I use persuasive words?

✓ Does my concluding statement make sense?

✓ Did I use correct grammar, spelling, capitalization, and punctuation?

Help children set goals and make a plan for improving in areas where their writing needs help.

STEP 5 Revise and Publish

Help children follow through with their plans for revision. If time permits, have children trade advertisements and offer suggestions for how to improve the writing.

Publishing Children can publish their advertisements by reading them to the class. They can also create a poster to go along with their advertisements and display them on the classroom wall.

Persuasive Text

Objectives

- Identify the characteristics of persuasive text.
- Write persuasive text, using facts and supporting reasons.
- Evaluate your writing.
- Revise and publish your writing.

 **Common Core State Standards**

Writing 1. Write opinion pieces in which they introduce the topic or name the book they are writing about, state an opinion, supply a reason for the opinion, and provide some sense of closure. **Writing 5.** With guidance and support from adults, focus on a topic, respond to questions and suggestions from peers, and add details to strengthen writing as needed.

STEP 1 Read Like a Writer

Review the key features of persuasive text listed below. Respond to any questions children might have.

Key Features of Persuasive Text
- States the writer's opinion about a topic
- Supports the opinion with facts and reasons
- Uses persuasive words such as *most* and *best*
- Often organizes reasons in order of importance
- Provides a concluding statement

Choose an opinion piece or persuasive text that children have already read to model key features. Display the model for children to see. Point out each key feature you have discussed.

STEP 2 Organize Your Ideas

Writing Prompt Look back at *Tippy-Toe Chick, Go!* and "Brave Little Cuckoo." Which bird is braver, Little Chick or Cuckoo? Write a short persuasive text that tells your opinion. Support your opinion with facts and reasons from the text. Include persuasive words such as *more* and *better.*

Think Aloud Your opinion will be more convincing if it is well organized. Decide on the opinion you will write about in your text. Then decide what facts and reasons you will use to support your opinion. You may wish to fill in a chart before you begin writing.

Guided Writing Display a chart with four boxes as an example. Show children how to write their opinion in the first box and then write the facts and reasons that support their opinion in the other three boxes. Explain to them that when they write, they will first state their opinion, then arrange their facts and reasons in a logical order, and finally end with a statement that sums up their opinion.

STEP 3 Draft Your Writing

Have children use their charts to write persuasive text. Remind them of the key features of persuasive text.

Think Aloud One of the best ways to persuade readers is to use facts and reasons to support your opinion. You can find facts and reasons by looking back at the selections. You also want to be sure you use persuasive words, such as *best* and *most.*

Getting Started Tell children to begin writing their persuasive texts using their charts to help them. Suggest supporting reasons for children having difficulty completing their ideas. Remind them to use persuasive words, and to end their texts with a concluding statement. Emphasize the importance of using correct grammar and complete sentences.

STEP 4 Evaluate Your Writing

Display the checklist below and have children use it to evaluate their persuasive texts. Circulate around the room and confer with individual children.

- ✓ Did I state my opinion clearly?
- ✓ Do my facts and reasons support my opinion?
- ✓ Did I use persuasive words?
- ✓ Does my concluding statement make sense?
- ✓ Did I use correct grammar, spelling, capitalization, and punctuation?

Help children set goals and make a plan for improving in areas where their writing needs help.

STEP 5 Revise and Publish

Help children follow through with their plans for revision. If time permits, have children trade texts and offer suggestions for how to improve the writing.

Publishing Children can publish their persuasive texts by reading them to the class or to small groups.

More Connect the Texts
Realistic Story

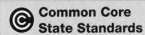
STEP 1 Read Like a Writer

Review the key features of a realistic story listed below. Respond to any questions children might have.

Key Features of a Realistic Story
- Has characters and a setting that seem real
- Tells events in order
- Has a beginning, middle, and end
- Uses words that make pictures for readers
- Uses time-order words

Use examples from *Sam, Come Back!* or another realistic story children are familiar with to model key features. Display the model for children to see, and point out each key feature you have discussed.

STEP 2 Organize Your Ideas

Writing Prompt Look back at *Sam, Come Back!* and *Get the Egg!* What do you think Brad and Kim would do if Sam knocked an egg from the nest? Write a realistic story telling what you think they would do. Use vivid details, such as colors and sounds, to make pictures for readers. Use time-order words such as *first, next,* and *last.* Cite evidence from the text to support the ideas in your story.

Think Aloud Your story will be more interesting if it is well organized. Decide what you will tell first, then next, and then last. Stories are also more interesting when they use vivid details, such as colors and sounds. Think of the details you will use in your story.

Guided Writing Display a sequence chart with three boxes as an example. Write *First* in the first box. Write *Next* in the second box. Write *Last* in the third box. Explain to children that when they write, they will begin their stories by telling what happens first. Then they will tell what happens next. Then they will finish the story by telling what happens last.

STEP 3 Draft Your Writing

Have children use their charts to write a short, realistic story. Remind them of the key features of a realistic story.

Think Aloud Stories that use vivid details can be more entertaining. Think of Sam. What does he look like? How does he act? Think of Brad and Kim. How do they look? How do they sound?

Getting Started Tell children to begin writing their realistic story using their charts to keep them on track. Remind them to use the time-order words *first, next,* and *last.* Give them suggestions on details they could use in their stories. Also emphasize the importance of using correct grammar and complete sentences.

STEP 4 Evaluate Your Writing

Display the checklist below and have children use it to evaluate their persuasive texts. Circulate around the room and confer with individual children.

✓ Does my story tell events that could really happen?

✓ Is my story told in order? Do I tell what happens first, next, and last?

✓ Did I include vivid details?

✓ Did I use correct grammar, spelling, capitalization, and punctuation?

Help children set goals and make a plan for improving in areas where their writing needs help.

STEP 5 Revise and Publish

Help children follow through with their plans for revision. If time permits, have children trade their stories and offer suggestions for how to improve the writing.

Publishing Children could post their stories on a class bulletin board or in a hall display case.

More Connect the Texts
Story Scene

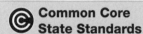
STEP 1 Read Like a Writer

Review the key features of a story scene listed below. Respond to any questions children might have.

Key Features of a Story Scene

- Uses make-believe characters
- Tells about a make-believe event
- Has a beginning, middle, and end
- Uses time-order words

Choose two scenes from a story that children are familiar with, such as *A Big Fish for Max*. Use scenes from the story, such as the fish man scene and the last scene, to model key features. Display the models for children to see. Point out each key feature you have discussed.

STEP 2 Organize Your Ideas

Writing Prompt Look back at *The Farmer in the Hat* and *The Big Circle*. Write two story scenes about two characters from *The Farmer in the Hat*. How would they work together to present a play of *The Big Circle?* Be sure both scenes have a beginning, a middle, and an end.

Think Aloud Story scenes are parts of a story. To plan story scenes, think of two characters from *The Farmer in the Hat*. Then think of things these two characters would do to prepare for a play of *The Big Circle*. You can fill in a chart to help you with your ideas.

Guided Writing Display a sequence chart with four boxes as an example. Label the first box *Characters*. Label the second box *Beginning*. Label the third box *Middle*. Label the last box *End of Scene*. Show children how to write their ideas for the first scene in each box. Then repeat the process for the second scene.

STEP 3 Draft Your Writing

Have children use their charts to write their story scenes. Remind them of the key features of a story scene.

Think Aloud When you write your story scenes, use your chart to help you stay on track. You can start at the beginning, then write the middle, and then write the end. Be sure to name your characters too. If you have any new ideas as you write, you can add them to your chart.

Getting Started Tell children to begin writing their story scenes using their charts to help them. Offer suggestions on how to finish their ideas if they are having trouble. Emphasize the importance of using correct grammar and complete sentences.

STEP 4 Evaluate Your Writing

Display the checklist below and have children use it to evaluate their scenes. Circulate around the room and confer with individual children.

✓ Did I use make-believe characters?

✓ Did I tell about a make-believe event?

✓ Do my scenes have a clear beginning, middle, and end?

✓ Did I use correct grammar, spelling, capitalization, and punctuation?

Help children set goals and make a plan for improving in areas where their writing needs help.

STEP 5 Revise and Publish

Help children follow through with their plans for revision. If time permits, have children trade story scenes and offer suggestions for how to improve the writing.

Publishing Children can publish their story scenes by reading them to the class. Children could also perform the scenes as short plays.

More Connect the Texts
Realistic Story

Objectives

- Identify the characteristics of a realistic story.
- Write a realistic story, using sensory details and temporal words.
- Evaluate your writing.
- Revise and publish your writing.

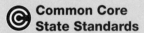

Common Core State Standards

Writing 3. Write narratives in which they recount two or more appropriately sequenced events, include some details regarding what happened, use temporal words to signal event order, and provide some sense of closure. **Writing 5.** With guidance and support from adults, focus on a topic, respond to questions and suggestions from peers, and add details to strengthen writing as needed.

STEP 1 Read Like a Writer

Review the key features of a realistic story listed below. Respond to any questions children might have.

Key Features of a Realistic Story

- Has characters and a setting that seem real
- Tells events in order
- Has a beginning, middle, and end
- Uses words that make pictures for readers
- Uses time-order words

Use examples from *A Place to Play* or another realistic story children are familiar with to model key features. Display the model for children to see. Point out each key feature you have discussed.

STEP 2 Organize Your Ideas

Writing Prompt Look back at *A Place to Play* and *The Class Pet.* Write a short, realistic story that tells how Benny would take care of a pet mouse. Use vivid details, such as colors and sounds, to make pictures for readers. Use time-order words such as *first, next,* and *last.*

Think Aloud Your story will be more interesting if it is well organized. Decide what you will tell first, then next, and then last. Stories are also more interesting when you use vivid details, such as colors and sounds. Think of the details you will use in your story.

Guided Writing Display a sequence chart with three boxes as an example. Write *First* in the first box. Write *Next* in the second box. Write *Last* in the third box. Explain to them that when they write, they will begin their stories by telling what happens first. Then they will tell what happens next. Then they will finish the story by telling what happens last.

STEP 3 Draft Your Writing

Have children use their charts to write a short, realistic story. Remind them of the key features of a realistic story.

Think Aloud Stories that use vivid details can be more entertaining. Think of Benny. What does he look like? How does he act? Think of a pet mouse. What does it need to live? What does it eat and drink?

Getting Started Tell children to begin writing their realistic stories using their charts to keep them on track. Remind them to use time-order words, such as *first, next,* and *last,* when writing the story's events. Also encourage them to use details in their writing, such as colors and sounds. Emphasize the importance of using correct grammar and complete sentences.

STEP 4 Evaluate Your Writing

Display the checklist below and have children use it to evaluate their realistic stories. Circulate around the room and confer with individual children.

✓ Does my story tell events that could really happen?

✓ Is my story told in order? Do I tell what happens first, next, and last?

✓ Did I include vivid details?

✓ Did I use correct grammar, spelling, capitalization, and punctuation?

Help children set goals and make a plan for improving in areas where their writing needs help.

STEP 5 Revise and Publish

Help children follow through with their plans for revision. If time permits, have children trade stories and offer suggestions for how to improve the writing.

Publishing Children could post their stories on a class bulletin board or in a hall display case.

Animal Fantasy

Objectives

- Identify the characteristics of an animal fantasy.
- Write an animal fantasy, using animals as characters.
- Evaluate your writing.
- Revise and publish your writing.

Common Core State Standards

Writing 3. Write narratives in which they recount two or more appropriately sequenced events, include some details regarding what happened, use temporal words to signal event order, and provide some sense of closure. **Writing 5.** With guidance and support from adults, focus on a topic, respond to questions and suggestions from peers, and add details to strengthen writing as needed.

STEP 1 Read Like a Writer

Review the key features of an animal fantasy listed below. Respond to any questions children might have.

Key Features of an Animal Fantasy

- Uses animals as characters
- Tells about make-believe events
- Tells details about events
- Has animals that do things real animals cannot do
- Uses time-order words
- Has a beginning, a middle, and an end

Choose an animal fantasy that children are familiar with, such as "The Ugly Duckling," to model key features. Display the model for children to see. Point out each key feature you have discussed.

STEP 2 Organize Your Ideas

Writing Prompt Look back at *Ruby in Her Own Time* and *Frog and Toad Together.* What do you think Toad would do if he met Ruby? Write an animal fantasy that tells what would happen. Be sure your fantasy has a beginning, a middle, and an end. Use time-order words, such as *first* and *next,* to show the order of events.

Think Aloud Your animal fantasies will be more entertaining if they are well organized. First, decide on the setting, or where the story takes place. Then decide what happens at the beginning, what happens in the middle, and what happens at the end. You can fill in a story map before you begin writing to help.

Guided Writing Display a chart with five boxes as an example. Write *Characters* in the first box and *Setting* in the second box. Write *Beginning* in the third box and *Middle* in the fourth. Write *End of Story* in the last box. Then show children how to fill in the story map. Explain to them that when they write, they will tell the events of the story in order using time-order words, such as *first* and *next.*

STEP 3 Draft Your Writing

Have children use their story maps to write their animal fantasies. Remind them of the key features of an animal fantasy.

Think Aloud Animal fantasies have characters that are animals. The animals do things that a real animal cannot do. What does Toad do that a real animal cannot do? What does Ruby do that a real animal cannot do? Do they speak? What do they say? You can add your details to your story map.

Getting Started Tell children to begin writing their animal fantasies using their maps to help them. Remind them to use time-order words, such as *first, next,* and *last,* when writing the story's events. Also encourage them to use details in their writing, such as colors and sounds. Emphasize the importance of using correct grammar and complete sentences.

STEP 4 Evaluate Your Writing

Display the checklist below and have children use it to evaluate their texts. Circulate around the room and confer with individual children.

✓ Did I use animals as characters?
✓ Did I include details about the events?
✓ Did I use time-order words?
✓ Did I use correct grammar, spelling, capitalization, and punctuation?

Help children set goals and make a plan for improving in areas where their writing needs help.

STEP 5 Revise and Publish

Help children follow through with their plans for revision. If time permits, have children trade fantasies and offer suggestions for how to improve the writing.

Publishing Children can publish their animal fantasies by reading them to the class. They could also present the story as a simple play for the class.

More Connect the Texts
Realistic Story

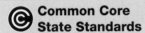

STEP 1 Read Like a Writer

Review the key features of a realistic story listed below. Respond to any questions children might have.

Key Features of a Realistic Story
- Has characters and a setting that seem real
- Tells events in order
- Has a beginning, middle, and end
- Uses words that make pictures for readers
- Uses time-order words

Choose examples of realistic stories that children are familiar with, such as *Peter's Chair,* to model key features. Display the model for children to see. Point out each key feature you have discussed.

STEP 2 Organize Your Ideas

Writing Prompt Look back at *A Trip to Washington, D.C.* and *Henry and Mudge and Mrs. Hopper's House.* What do you think Henry and Mudge would do if they visited Washington, D.C.? Write a realistic story telling what you think they would do. Use vivid details, such as colors and sounds, to make pictures for readers. Use time-order words such as *first, next,* and *last.*

Think Aloud Your story will be more interesting if it is well organized. Decide what you will tell first, then next, and then last. Stories are also more interesting when they use vivid details, such as colors and sounds. Think of the details you will use in your story. Where do you think Henry and Mudge would go during their visit? What do you think they would do?

Guided Writing Display a sequence chart with three boxes as an example. Write *First* in the first box. Write *Next* in the second box. Write *Last* in the third box. Explain to them that when they write, they will begin their stories by telling what happens first. Then they will tell what happens next. Then they will finish the story by telling what happens last.

STEP 3 Draft Your Writing

Have children use their charts to write a short, realistic story. Remind them of the key features of a realistic story.

Think Aloud Stories that use vivid details can be more entertaining. Think of Henry. What does he look like? How does he act? Think of Mudge. Think of Washington, D.C. How does it look?

Getting Started Tell children to begin writing their realistic story using their charts to guide them. Remind them to use time-order words, such as *first, next,* and *last,* when writing the story's events. Suggest details they could use in their stories. Also remind them to use correct grammar and complete sentences.

STEP 4 Evaluate Your Writing

Display the checklist below and have children use it to evaluate their realistic stories. Circulate around the room and confer with individual children.

✓ Does my story tell events that could really happen?

✓ Is my story told in order? Do I tell what happens first, next, and last?

✓ Did I include vivid details?

✓ Did I use correct grammar, spelling, capitalization, and punctuation?

Help children set goals and make a plan for improving in areas where their writing needs help.

STEP 5 Revise and Publish

Help children follow through with their plans for revision. If time permits, have children trade their stories and offer suggestions for how to improve the writing.

Publishing Children can publish their realistic stories as a class anthology. Children can use a computer to print a final draft of their stories. They can also draw a picture to accompany their printouts. Then all the stories can be placed in a binder.

More Connect the Texts
Animal Fantasy

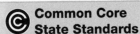
STEP 1 Read Like a Writer

Review the key features of an animal fantasy listed below. Respond to any questions children might have.

Key Features of an Animal Fantasy

- Uses animals as characters
- Tells about make-believe events
- Tells details about events
- Has animals that do things real animals cannot do
- Uses time-order words
- Has a beginning, a middle, and an end

Choose an animal fantasy with which children are familiar, such as "Little Red Hen," to model key features. Display the model for children to see. Point out each key feature you have discussed.

STEP 2 Organize Your Ideas

Writing Prompt Look back at *Tippy-Toe Chick, Go!* and *Dot & Jabber and the Great Acorn Mystery.* Imagine Dot and Jabber meet Dog. Write an animal fantasy that tells what would happen. Be sure your fantasy has a beginning, a middle, and an end. Use time-order words, such as *first* and *next,* to show the order of events. Use details from the text.

Think Aloud Your animal fantasy will be more entertaining if it is well organized. First, decide on the setting, or where the story takes place. Then decide what happens at the beginning, what happens in the middle, and what happens at the end. You can fill in a story map before you begin writing to help.

Guided Writing Display a chart with five boxes as an example. Write *Characters* in the first box and *Setting* in the second box. Write *Beginning* in the third box and *Middle* in the fourth. Write *End of Story* in the last box. Then show children how to fill in the story map. Explain to them that when they write, they will tell the events of the story in order using time-order words, such as *first* and *next.*

STEP 3 Draft Your Writing

Have children use their story maps to write their animal fantasies. Remind them of the key features of an animal fantasy.

Think Aloud Animal fantasies have characters that are animals. The animals do things that real animals cannot do. What do Dot and Jabber do that real animals cannot do? What does Dog do that a real animal cannot do? Do they speak? What do they say? You can add your details to your story map.

Getting Started Tell children to begin writing their animal fantasies using their maps to help them. Remind them to use time-order words, such as *first, next,* and *last,* when writing the story's events. Also encourage them to use details in their writing, such as colors and sounds. Emphasize the importance of using correct grammar and complete sentences.

STEP 4 Evaluate Your Writing

Display the checklist below and have children use it to evaluate their texts. Circulate around the room and confer with individual children.

✓ Did I use animals as characters?

✓ Did I include details about the events?

✓ Did I use time-order words?

✓ Did I use correct grammar, spelling, capitalization, and punctuation?

Help children set goals and make a plan for improving in areas where their writing needs help.

STEP 5 Revise and Publish

Help children follow through with their plans for revision. If time permits, have children trade fantasies and offer suggestions for how to improve the writing.

Publishing Children can publish their animal fantasies by reading them in small groups. They can also draw pictures to go along with their stories and present the pictures along with the stories in a binder or folder.